Mighty Men

Mighty Men

by

ELEANOR FARJEON

WITH AN INTRODUCTION BY

C. C. BARNES

SUPERVISOR OF SOCIAL SCIENCE IN THE DETROIT PUBLIC SCHOOLS

PICTURES BY

HUGH CHESTERMAN

Preface

In learning history, or indeed in learning
anything, there are certain things which we may
know to be true. But there are many things which
may not be true, or only partly true; tales,
incidents, and legends which have grown out of
the known facts, and which, if they are not as true
as the facts, may have a still greater power than
these in waking the imagination of a very young
child. And unless the child's imagination is
wakened, so that it moves like a light through the
things he must learn, what he gathers from his
learning will only be the dried specimens from his
teacher's collection, and not the living flower he
has smelt for himself.

For this reason, I have not hesitated to include
among my stories many touches, and even some
whole stories, which are the poet's rather than the

historian's. But they have come down to us because they have something in them that outlasts history, and is as living in us now as it was in the men who expressed it long ago. We may say that the story of Alexander is, on the whole, true, and that of Achilles is not; yet the story of Achilles stirred the soul of Alexander, and made history as surely as did any conquest of Philip of Macedon. To begin with, it is better to captivate a child's fancy than to teach his mind. Once he has come to believe in Hannibal and Xerxes as he does in Puss in Boots, he will delight in any further facts about them.

So I have not tried to present any part of my tales as more or less true than the rest. To do that would be the undoing of the whole chain of stories. And if the legends are not the very tree of history, they are the birds that sing in the tree, and will go on building their nests there, year after year, till the tree itself is dead.

E. F.

Contents

PART I: FROM ACHILLES TO JULIUS CÆSAR

PART II: FROM BEOWULF TO WILLIAM THE CONQUEROR

List of Stories

Introduction

Within recent years the demand for supplementary reading material has been met by authors and publishers in a fine way. History stories rake up much of this literature, and this is only natural. In the first place, history is the record of life itself, and the stories that are selected are the most thrilling, dramatic, and inspiring acts of the great drama.

In teaching history to boys and girls from ten to twelve years old simple material must be used. Children of that age like action. They crave the dramatic, the picturesque, the personal.

Mighty Men by Eleanor Farjeon is made up of such stories. Miss Farjeon has presented these stories in a delightfully fresh form. She first tells the story of some hero of ancient times and then follows it with a short, bright poem which impresses the story on the young reader's memory in a fashion that could be done in no other way.

These characters are shown in thrilling action like a motion picture. The word pictures are vivid. At one time the reader is in the tent with the sulking Achilles, and at another on the walls of Troy with Priam and Hecuba watching their favorite son Hector fight the great Achilles. You cheer the boy Alexander as he rides the wild Bucephalus, and you cross the Alps with Hannibal.

The stories in *Mighty Men* are not mere exploits scattered through history but are given in chronological order, thus affording a solid foundation for all the child's future knowledge of history.

This book is a supplementary reader and can be used in the middle grades. All a teacher will need to do will be to turn a child loose in the book and let him read. No assignments need be made. The stories have the charm of lively presentation. Each story calls for more.

If more supplementary material like the stories in *Mighty Men* was furnished, more children would come to like history. One of our tasks as teachers should be to make boys and girls like the type of literature that most people read. Then why not give them the type of stories that will accomplish this?

Mighty Men will not be and should not be read and laid aside like an ordinary story book. It will be read and reread until its stories become a part of the child's thinking.

Some books are suited only for silent reading. *Mighty Men* is an excellent silent reader, and it has the additional value of being exceedingly well suited for reading aloud.

Children and adults too like pictures. The stories in this book have been delightfully illustrated by Hugh Chesterman. As graphic as Miss Farjeon is in her story-telling, such illustrations as those representing Alexander and Bucephalus, King Olaf in the deck of the Long Serpent, and the finding of Romulus and Remus by the wolf cannot help but make the stories more real.

C. C. Barnes

Part I

From Achilles to Julius Cæsar

To Olga's
Jessica Mary

The Friend of Achilles

THERE WAS ONCE a city in Asia called Troy. King Priam was King, and he had many sons, of whom Hector was the first, and Paris was the fairest.

And over the water there were Kings in the cities of Greece. The chief of them was Agamemnon, the King of Argos. His brother Menelaus, the King of Sparta, had for his wife the most beautiful woman in the world. Her name was Helen.

One day Prince Paris of Troy came over the water to visit the King of Sparta; and because he was so fair, and because she was so beautiful, he and Queen Helen loved each other, and he took her down to his ship and sailed away with her to Troy.

Then King Agamemnon was angry for his brother's sake, and all the Kings of Greece and the

Isles of Greece came at his call to make war on Troy, and bring Queen Helen back again. There was Ulysses, who was the wisest King in Greece; and Ajax the giant, who was the strongest; and Achilles, whose mother Thetis was a sea nymph. With Achilles came Patroclus, his friend whom he loved. And there were many more besides. They came with all their ships and men, and they fought for ten years around the walls of Troy.

The Kings and Princes of Greece camped with their tents and soldiers on the plain between Troy and the sea; and on the shores of the sea they kept their ships, propped up with mighty stones, all ready to sail away when the battle was won and Queen Helen got back. But it seemed as though the battle never would end, and before it was ended King Agamemnon quarreled with Achilles, the man whom Troy feared most. After the quarrel Achilles sat in his tent and said he would fight no more. For, as well as being the greatest fighter, Achilles had the angriest temper of them all. But he was never angry with his friend Patroclus.

There came a day when the Greeks and the Trojans met in a great battle outside the walls of Troy. Many chiefs on both sides were killed, and many wounded, and sometimes the Greeks had the better of the fight, and sometimes the Trojans. At last Hector, King Priam's eldest son, leapt into the light with a spear in each hand and his eyes flashing fire; and he called on the men of Troy to follow him to the Grecian ships and burn them on the shore, so that the Greeks could not escape. Then up stood Ajax, the giant of the Greeks; and seeing the Trojans coming, he ran to defend the ships, crying:

"Come near, Hector! Come if you dare! We will burn Troy before you burn our ships!"

But King Agamemnon was suddenly afraid, and he said: "Would it not be better to launch the ships and sail away to Greece? The Trojans are too strong for us."

Then Ulysses, the wise King of Ithaca, answered: "Now surely, Agamemnon, you should be ashamed to speak to us so! What! shall we go away from Troy, after fighting so long and suffering so much? Why, even as we launched the ships, the men of Troy would fall on us and kill us."

"You speak well," said Agamemnon, and returned to the battle, where Ajax stood in the ship's prow, thrusting with his great spear at the

Trojans, who came with torches of fire to burn the ships. And nearer and nearer came Hector, till he laid his hand on the ship's stem, and Ajax was driven back to the seats of the rowers; and Ajax the giant cried to the men of Greece:

"O Greeks, bear yourselves like men! For there are no walls to shelter us, only the sea behind us, and we are far from our homes. Our only hope lies in being brave!"

Now while the battle went so badly for the Greeks, Achilles, who might have saved them, still sulked in his tent, and Patroclus his friend stood near him, weeping bitterly.

"Why do you stand there crying like a girl?" asked Achilles.

"O Achilles," said Patroclus, "if you will not fight yourself, lend me your glorious armor that your mother Thetis gave you, and let me go into the battle armed like yourself; for though I cannot fight as well as you, the sight of your arms may terrify the Trojans and give heart to the Greeks."

Achilles consented, and Patroclus put on Achilles' wonderful armor and went into the fight. And so fiercely Patroclus fought, that he drove the Trojans back from the Grecian ships, and chased

"We will burn Troy before you burn our ships."

them over the plain to the city of Troy. Patroclus followed them, longing to kill Hector. Three times he rushed at the Trojan army, and each time slew nine chiefs. The fourth time a blow struck him and darkened his eyes, and his helmet fell off, and he turned to go back to the Greeks; but Hector saw him, and thrust with his spear, and Patroclus fell dying at his feet. And Hector, looking down on him, said:

"Not even the armor of Achilles can help you now, Patroclus."

Then Patroclus answered: "Boast no more, Hector! for even as I die I see that your own hour draws near, and before long Achilles himself will kill you."

So saying, he died; and Hector, gazing down upon him, said:

"Who can tell? Perhaps I myself will kill Achilles."

He took Achilles' wonderful armor off the body of Patroclus and put it on himself. And the horses of Achilles stood by and wept for the death of Patroclus.

THE HORSES OF ACHILLES

The Horses of Achilles,
With their proud and kingly manes,
They stood beside Patroclus
Upon the Trojan plains.

They stood beside Patroclus
A-weeping for the dead,
Big tears rolled down their faces,
And each Horse bowed his head.

Each Horse bowed his head
To the dusty Trojan plains,
And in the dust lay trailing
Their proud and kingly manes.

The Death of Hector

ACHILLES SAT IN his tent and sulked, while the battle raged outside. And one of the Greek chiefs came running in to Achilles and said, weeping:

"I bring sad news, Achilles! Patroclus is dead, killed by Hector."

Then Achilles gave a great cry and fell down in his grief for his friend Patroclus, whom he loved; and he tore his rich purple clothes, and put the dust of the earth and the ashes of the fire on his golden hair, and would have killed himself for sorrow, if another had not held his hands. Far off in the depths of the sea where she lived, his mother Thetis heard his cry and came to him and said:

"Why do you weep, my son?"

"Ah, mother!" cried Achilles, "Patroclus my friend is dead, and Hector has my armor that I gave him to wear; and unless I can kill Hector I do not wish to live."

"You cannot fight without armor," said Thetis; "tomorrow I will bring you some even more glorious than the last."

In the morning she came back with a shining shield, covered with pictures of fields and cities, of grapes and corn and rivers, and men fighting and dancing and tending their sheep; she also brought a breastplate that was brighter than fire, and a helmet with a golden crest. Achilles lay in his tent, mourning beside the body of Patroclus, but when he saw the wonderful armor his eyes blazed with fire, and he sprang up and put it on. Then he rushed out, and shouted to the Greek chiefs to come with him; and when they came he took Agamemnon's hand and said:

"Let us forget our quarrel, for I am angry no longer, but am going back to the battle, to drive the Trojans away."

All the Greeks shouted for joy, and Achilles mounted his chariot and drove his swift horses straight into the battle, seeking for Hector. At first he could not find him, but he fought so fiercely that all the Trojans turned and fled away to the city. King Priam of Troy stood on a tower on the wall, and saw them coming, and he called to the keepers of the gates:

"Keep the gates open that our people may come in, for they are flying from Achilles."

And the keepers did so, till all the Trojans were safe inside—all but Hector, King Priam's bravest son, who would not fly, but waited outside the walls of Troy to meet Achilles.

Then King Priam, his father, called to him from the tower on the walls of Troy:

"Do not stay there alone, Hector, my dearest son, to meet Achilles in his fury! Many of my sons have been killed in the battle, but if you die too my grief will be greater than for any of the others. Save your dear self, and save me, your old father, from sorrow."

And Queen Hecuba, his mother, stood on the tower beside Priam and wept, and cried:

"O Hector, my son, have pity on me! Remember how I comforted you when you were a baby, and do not wait out there alone to meet the great Achilles!"

And Hector heard them, but would not go in, saying to himself: "I should be ashamed to go into the city and hide myself. I must either kill Achilles or die by his hand, fighting for Troy."

Even as he thought this, Achilles rushed towards him in all his bright armor, with the golden crest nodding in his helmet, and the fight began. Round the walls of Troy they ran, and under fig trees along the great road, and past the two fountains of the river where, in times of peace, the Trojan women used to wash their clothes. Three times around the city ran the two heroes. At last they came face to face, and Hector said:

"Now, Achilles, one of us must die; but let us agree that if I kill you I will not hurt or shame your body, but will give it back to the Greeks; and you must promise to do the same, if you kill me."

But Achilles, full of hate because Hector had killed his friend, replied:

"Talk not to me of promises, Hector! Lions make no promises to the sheep they kill, and I will make none to you!"

Achilles threw his great spear, but Hector stooped, and it flew over his head. And Hector threw his spear, and it struck the very middle of Achilles' shield; but the shield was too strong to be pierced. Then Hector drew his sword, and ran

*Achilles . . . drove his swift horses
straight into the battle, seeking for Hector.*

to meet Achilles, but before he could strike him Achilles struck first, and Hector fell dead on the ground. Then Achilles in his hate tied Hector's feet together, and bound them to the back of his chariot, and so drove back to the Grecian camp, dragging the body of Hector in the dust. And Priam his father, and Hecuba his mother, saw it from the walls of Troy, and wailed aloud; and all the people of Troy wailed too. And Hector's wife heard the wailing, and ran to the wall and looked; and when she saw the horses of Achilles dragging her husband's body over the plain, she fainted on the wall.

But in the night King Priam rode out of the city, alone, with many presents and much gold in his chariot, and he came in the dark to the tent of Achilles, and knelt before him and kissed his hands, saying:

"Think of your father, Achilles, and pity me! Nineteen sons I had, and nearly all are dead, and now you have slain Hector, who was the best of all. I bring you gold and presents in exchange for his body. Have pity on me, and give it back to me."

And Achilles was filled with pity and gave Priam the body of Hector, and he brought it back to Troy; and the people saw him coming and opened the gates, and every man and woman in Troy came out to meet him. And they brought the body of Hector home, and buried it with honor.

KING PRIAM IN THE DARK NIGHT WENT

King Priam in the dark night went
And entered great Achilles' tent.

King Priam in his golden crown
Before Achilles' feet knelt down.

King Priam said: "The deed is done,
But give me back my own dead son."

King Priam said: "Your hands I kiss,
The hands that brought my son to this.

"And oh, Achilles," said the King,
"Is it not a sorry thing

"To see a father kiss again
The hands by which his son was slain?"

"King Priam take away your dead,
And go in peace," Achilles said.

The Burning of Troy

FOR TEN YEARS the Greek heroes camped outside the city of Troy, and made war on it; and for ten years the Trojan heroes lived inside the city of Troy and defended it. The greatest hero of all the Trojans was Hector, the King's son, and the second greatest was Æneas, who was also a Prince. Then Hector was killed in battle by the great Achilles, and Æneas was the chief hero in Troy. But even he could not save Troy.

The Greeks thought of a trick for getting into the city. They made a great wooden horse, big enough to hide men in its body, and they left it outside the gates of Troy; and the Trojans thought it was a fine toy, and took it into the city. In the night the Greeks who were hidden in the horse crept out, and opened the city gates, and all the other Greeks came in and took the city, and killed the King, and made the women prisoners, and burned the houses.

Æneas saw all this, but could not help. What could one man do? So he ran through the burning city to find his wife, Creusa, and his old father Anchises, and his little son Ascanius, to save them if he could. They were waiting for him in his house, and Æneas said:

"Come away with me to the hills."

But his old father Anchises said:

"No, I will not go. Save yourself, Æneas, if you can, for you are young and strong, and still have your life to live. But I am old, and my life is nearly over, and l have nothing more to hope for. So let me stay and die in Troy where I have lived."

Æneas answered his father: "I will not save myself and leave you. If you will not come with me, I will go back and fight in the streets until I die." And he turned to go.

Then Creusa, his wife, stopped him and said:

"If you are going out to die, take me and Ascanius to die with you; but if you have any hope of saving us, stay here, and guard us all in the house." And she held out their little son to him in her arms.

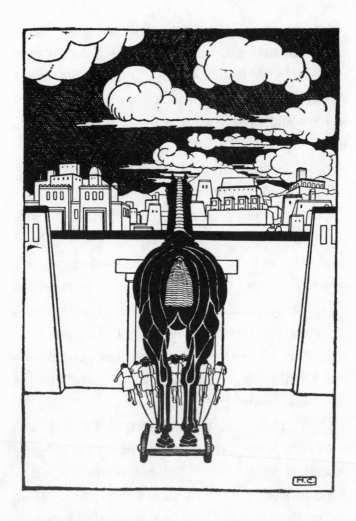

The Trojans took it into the city.

Then a strange thing happened. A light began to shine from the head of the child Ascanius, glittering in his curls and playing on his face. When he saw it, his old grandfather gave a cry of joy and raised his hands to the sky and prayed:

"Oh for a sign that this means happiness and hope for me and my family!"

As he prayed there came a clap of thunder, and then a star shot across the sky, and passed over the city, and vanished in the distant woods.

And old Anchises said: "Now I will go with you, Æneas; let us follow the star, for it will lead us all to something good."

The city of Troy burned brighter, the heat grew greater, and Æneas knew they must make haste. He put a lion skin on his shoulders, lifted his old father on his back, took his little son by the hand, and told his wife to follow him. So they left the house, and went through the burning city, taking with them all the Trojans they could find who were still alive. But when they were safe outside the city Æneas saw that Creusa was not with them. Then his heart was full of fear, and he told the Trojans to guard his old father and his little son while he ran back to find her.

And though Troy was full of the Greeks, he ran through the burning streets, calling his wife by her name. At last he saw her coming toward him, but she looked bigger and more beautiful than he had ever seen her when she was alive; and so he knew that she had died, and this was her spirit.

She smiled at him and said: "You must not weep, Æneas, for it was not Heaven's will that I should go with you on your journey. You have a long journey to make now and you must build ships, and sail away over many seas to the land of Italy, where the river Tiber flows through a beautiful land, full of vines and olives. There you will live in peace at last, and you will marry a King's daughter, and be the first of a great new race of men. Farewell now; and always love our son Ascanius."

Then Creusa vanished like a dream, and Æneas went away with his father and his son into the mountains. There he and his men built ships for the long journey, and when they were ready they sailed away to Italy. Many adventures and dangers they met with on the way, and Æneas was often tempted to bring his ships ashore and rest. But he always remembered Creusa's words, that he must rest only in Italy. One day he came to a seashore where the beautiful Queen Dido was building the city of Carthage. Æneas stayed a while and helped her build it, and she wanted him to stay forever and be the King of Carthage. But Carthage was not Italy, so once more Æneas sailed away, and when she saw him go Queen Dido made a great fire and burned herself for sorrow.

At last, after many years, Æneas came to the lovely land of Italy, where golden oranges and yellow lemons grow on the trees, the green corn springs under the olive groves, and the white and purple grapes grow on the hillside.

And the King of Italy, whose name was Latinus, welcomed him, and gave him his daughter Lavinia for a wife. And there the little Ascanius, when he grew to be a man, built the city of Alba on the banks of a lake, and Æneas and his sons were the Kings of the land.

QUEEN DIDO IS BUILDING

Queen Dido is building.
What is she building?
She's building up Carthage so stately and tall,
Who, then, will help her?
Æneas will help her
To raise the high turrets on Carthage and all.

Queen Dido is weeping.
Why is she weeping?
She's weeping for somebody stately and tall.
Who, then, will hear her?
Æneas will hear her
As he sails o'er the ocean from Carthage and all.

The Bow of Ulysses

OF ALL THE GRECIAN chiefs who fought against Troy, Ulysses, King of Ithaca, was the most cunning and clever. It was he who thought of the plan of the wooden horse, by which the Greeks at last got into Troy and conquered the city, and so won the great war that had lasted for ten years.

After this the Grecian Kings prepared to return to their own cities which they had not seen for so long; and Ulysses got into his ship with his men and sailed away to Ithaca, for he was eager to see again his beautiful wife Penelope, and his son Telemachus, who had been only a little boy when Ulysses came to Troy. But before Ulysses got back to Ithaca another ten years passed, for his journey was full of danger and adventures, and it was only his cunning that saved him many times from death.

At last, after a great shipwreck, he lost all his friends and sailors, and he found himself alone on the great sea on a raft made of trees. Then once again a storm came on him and broke his raft, and for two days and nights he swam in the rough sea. Presently he was thrown up on a strange shore where he lay in the bushes, worn out with his troubles, and slept.

In the morning the Princess of the land came down with her maidens to wash the linen. She was the fairest and sweetest Princess ever heard of, and her name was Nausicaa. When the linen was washed and spread on the shore to dry, Nausicaa and her maidens played at ball, and sang as they played.

But presently she threw the ball too far, and it fell into a stream. The maidens cried aloud, and their cries awoke Ulysses, who came out of the bushes, all dressed in leaves, for his own clothes had been lost in the wild sea. At sight of him the maidens fled away; only Nausicaa stayed. Ulysses knelt before her and begged her not to fear him, and to give him a garment with which to clothe himself. The lovely Princess took him back to the city, and there he was given food and clothes by the King; he told them all his story, and how he was longing to return to Ithaca and see his wife and son again. So the King sent him to Ithaca in one of his own ships, laden with riches and presents, and at last, after twenty years, Ulysses stood once more on his own land.

But his troubles were not yet ended, for during the twenty years, many Princes and strong men had come wooing his wife, Penelope.

"Ulysses is dead," they said, "and you must choose another husband."

They sat in the palace, eating and drinking, and behaving as though they owned the land, and would not go away. But Penelope wished for no other husband than Ulysses, who she thought was dead, so she told the suitors that before she married again she must finish a great picture, which she was weaving on her loom. All day she wove, but at night she came secretly and undid all the day's work, so that the picture was never finished.

At last the suitors found out her trick, and they were angrier and ruder than ever, and her heart was full of fear and sorrow, for she did not know how to put them off any longer. So she said she would marry the one of them that could bend Ulysses' great bow, and hit a mark with his arrow.

When Ulysses reached Ithaca he heard this story from his old swineherd. So he disguised himself in rags, and went up to the palace, and nobody knew who he was. Only his old dog, Argus, knew him. Argus had been a puppy when he sailed away for Troy, and had waited twenty years, watching for his master's return. Now he was old and ill, and as soon as he saw Ulysses he wagged his tail and died for joy.

Then Ulysses went into the palace, and came among the suitors like a beggar, and they mocked at him, not knowing who he was. Even Penelope did not know him in his rags, when she came into the hall with his great bow, which none but he had ever been able to bend.

One after another the suitors tried to bend and shoot with it; but none was strong enough. They rubbed the string with oil, and warmed the bow at the fire, but all in vain.

Then Ulysses said: "Let me try the bow, for once I was a strong man, and perhaps I still have some strength."

The suitors were angry that an old beggar

One after another he shot the wicked suitors.

should make such a request, but Penelope gave him the bow and the arrows. And Ulysses stood up in all his strength at the end of the hall and drew back the bowstrings; and one after another he shot the wicked suitors as they sat at the feast. They sprang up to fight him, but he was too strong for them, and soon they all lay slain at his feet.

Then he turned to Penelope, who wondered still who this strange and mighty beggar might be, and he said:

"My Queen and my wife! I am Ulysses, your husband."

And she knew him at last in spite of his rags, and ran to him and embraced him.

And that is how, at the end of twenty years, Ulysses came home again.

ARGUS

Argus was a puppy,
Frisking full of joy.
Ulysses was his master,
Who sailed away to Troy.

Argus on the seashore
Watched the ship's white track,
And barked a little puppy-bark
To bring his master back.

Argus was an old dog,
Too gray and tried for tears.
He lay outside the house-door
And watched for twenty years.

When twenty years were ended
Ulysses came from Troy.
Argus wagged an old dog's wag,
And then he died for joy.

Queen Esther

THIS IS THE tale of the King with two names. One of his names was a very long name, and his other name was Xerxes.

Xerxes was a King in Asia, and he ruled over a hundred and twenty-seven countries, from the land of the brown-skinned Indians to the land of the black-skinned people. He was rich and mighty and proud of his riches, and he wanted every one to admire him and his might, so he made a great feast for the nobles and the Princes in all his countries; and when they came he showed them his riches, and asked all the people in, both great and small.

They had the feast in the court of the palace garden, with its pillars of marble, and curtains of white, green, and blue, with purple cords and silver rings; and the couches were of gold and silver, and the pavement was of colored marble, red, and blue, and white, and black. And there they sat and drank the King's wine from golden goblets.

On the seventh day of the feast the King was merry with drinking, and he said: "Let Vashti, my Queen, be sent for, that I may show her to the Princes and the people in her beauty; for my other treasures they have seen, but she is the fairest of all."

But Queen Vashti was angry at being sent for to be made a show of, and refused to come.

Now the King had a black temper when he did not get his own way, and he cried:

"Vashti shall no longer be my Queen! I will send her away and choose another Queen from the fairest maidens in the land."

And he sent Vashti away, and messengers went forth bidding all the loveliest maidens in the city to come before the King.

The loveliest of all was a young Jewess called Esther, who lived with her cousin, old Mordecai. There were many Jews living here and there in the land, but the other people did not like them, and treated them badly. So when Esther's time came to go before the King, Mordecai advised her not to let him know she was a Jewess, and she did as he advised. She was so beautiful that the King loved her better than any of the others and made her his Queen. But nobody knew that Queen Esther was a Jewess. And her old cousin Mordecai sat humbly at the King's gate, and watched her pass in and out of the palace.

As he sat there, he heard the talk of the people who went in and out; and one day two of the King's servants whispered together that they meant to kill the King. The next time Esther passed, Mordecai stood up in the gate and told her; and Queen Esther told the King how Mordecai had overheard the plot, and the King had the two servants hanged on a tree.

Now the King had among his courtiers a favorite whose name was Haman, and no one hated the Jews so much as Haman did. The King gave Haman great honors, and ordered that all his servants should bow whenever he went by. But when Haman went in and out of the King's gate, Mordecai never bowed; he just sat where he was. Then Haman was angry; he knew Mordecai was a Jew, and he thought of a plan to punish all the Jews, and Mordecai among them. So he went to

When Haman went in and out of the King's Gate,
Mordecai never bowed.

the King and said:

"There are certain people, called Jews, who have no country of their own but are scattered here and there through all your countries; but they have their own laws, and do not obey yours, and it would be better for you not to keep them. So send forth papers saying they must all be killed, and I will, myself, give you ten thousand talents of silver to pay for the killing."

And the King gave his ring to Haman, for that was the sign of his power, and told him to write out the papers saying the Jews must all be killed on the thirteenth day of the twelfth month. Haman sent the papers into all the King's countries, sealed with the King's ring; and the Jews read how they were to be killed when the day came. But Queen Esther, inside the palace, knew nothing of the danger to her own people.

Then Mordecai, who had read the paper, dressed himself in sackcloth and poured ashes on his head and went through the city with a loud and bitter cry till he came to the King's gate; and he sent in word to Esther of the plot, and bade her beg the King to save the Jews, who were her own people.

And Esther said: "I may not go to the King unless he sends for me; for it is the Law that anyone who approaches the King of his own accord must die, unless the King holds out his golden scepter towards him. But I will take the risk. I will go to the King, though he has not sent for me; and if I die, I die."

Then Esther put on her royal robes and went to the King's house; and when the King saw her standing so beautiful in his court, he was pleased with her, and held out his golden scepter, and said:

"What wilt thou, Queen Esther, and what is thy request? It shall be even given to thee to the half of my kingdom."

And Esther said: "I beg that the King and Haman will come tonight to the banquet I have prepared."

So that night the King and Haman supped with Queen Esther, and as they sat drinking the King asked again: "What wilt thou, Queen Esther, and what is thy request? Even to the half of my kingdom, it is thine."

But Esther only said: "I beg that the King and Haman will sup with me again tomorrow night."

And Haman went away puffed up with pride,

because he alone had been asked to sup twice with the King and Queen. And he had a gallows built ready to hang Mordecai, fifty cubits high.

Now that night as the King was looking through some papers, he found one telling how Mordecai had once saved him from a plot, and he thought: "Mordecai saved my life, yet I have done him no honor for it." And he sent at once for Haman and asked him: "What shall be done to the man whom the King delights to honor?"

Then Haman thought in his heart: "The King must mean me!" And he said: "The King's own clothes should be put on that man, and the King's crown on his head, and he should ride on the King's own horse through the city, and the noblest Prince should go before him crying: 'This is the man the King delights to honor!'"

Then the King said: "Mordecai is the man; do all this as you have said, and ride before him yourself through the city, crying that he is the man I delight to honor."

And Haman was full of shame and anger, but he had to do it, while Mordecai rode through the city on the King's horse, wearing the King's crown.

When it was done, Mordecai sat once more in the King's gate, but Haman hurried to his own house, full of anger.

Then came the second night when the King and Haman supped with Queen Esther. And as they sat at supper the King said: "What wilt thou, Queen Esther, and what is thy request? Let it be even the half of my kingdom!"

Then Esther knelt before the King and said: "O King, I beg of you my life, and the life of my people, for we have an enemy who wants to kill us."

And the King said: "Who is the enemy that dares do this to thee?"

And Esther answered: "He is this wicked Haman!"

The King was so full of wrath, that he sprang up and walked in the garden, and there he saw over the wall the tall gallows which Haman had built the day before.

He asked a servant: "What is that?" And the servant said: "It is the gallows Haman built for Mordecai, who saved the King's life."

Then the King said: "Hang Haman on it!"

So they hanged Haman on his own gallows, fifty

cubits high. And the King sent for Mordecai to come into the palace, and he gave him his own ring, which he had taken from Haman, and made him next to himself in power over the people.

PUT ON YOUR PURPLE, ESTHER!

Put on your purple, Esther, Esther;
Esther, put on your crown of gold,
And go and wait
By the King's own gate—
For your people will perish, Esther, Esther,
Unless your heart is bold!

She put on her purple and crown, did Esther;
Esther she did as she was told.
She broke the Law.
But the King, who saw,
Said, "She is beautiful, Esther, Esther!"
And held out his rod of gold.

King Xerxes Goes to War

THIS IS THE Tale of Xerxes, the King with two names.

King Xerxes of Persia was rich and proud and cruel. His palace was full of gold; he had a great country and ruled over many people, and he longed for still more gold, and still more land, and still more people to command. On the other side of the sea lay the country of Greece, and King Xerxes in Persia looked towards it and said:

"I will conquer Greece, and the countries around Greece, and I will be King of the world as far as the sky can be seen. The sun will then shine on no land but mine."

His uncle heard him, and said: "O King Xerxes, you are greater than all the Persians who have ever lived, and greater than all the Persians who have never been born!"

Then Xerxes called up his army from all the people whom he ruled. It took him four years to get all his soldiers together, the food to feed them on the march, the animals to carry the food, the chariots for the commanders to ride in, and the ships for them to sail in." For this was the greatest army that had ever been seen—it was even greater than the army and the ships of the Grecian Kings who went to fight against Troy.

The soldiers came from all parts of Asia, and had all sorts of clothes and armor. Some had shields of leather, and some had shields of wicker; some had helmets of brass, and some had helmets of wood; some had spears, some had bows and arrows, some had short daggers; some had their legs bound in purple bands, and some wore shirts covered with iron scales like the scales of a fish. The Phoenicians came in ships, the Indians in chariots drawn by wild asses; the Arabians rode on camels.

And most splendid of all were the Ten Thousand Persians, the King's own bodyguard. He called them the Immortals, because they were as tall and strong as gods. They glittered all over with gold. On the points of their spears they carried golden

The Arabians rode on camels.

apples and silver pomegranates, and they marched with garlands on their heads. Behind them rode King Xerxes in his golden chariot, the proudest, haughtiest King in all the world. He believed that nobody could conquer him; he believed that he was more powerful than the sea and the mountains; he believed that he had the right to kill anyone he hated and reward any one who pleased him.

One day, on his great march to the sea, King Xerxes saw a beautiful plane tree.

"Stop!" said Xerxes to his army. And his army stopped.

"O Plane Tree!" said Xerxes, "I have never seen so beautiful a Tree as you! I will reward you for being so beautiful." And he gave the plane tree presents of golden ornaments to hang on it. For when King Xerxes was pleased with men, he gave them golden presents; so why not a tree?

"Go on!" said Xerxes to his army. And his army went on.

At last they came to the sea, and King Xerxes told his men to build a bridge of ships from side to side, so that his whole army might march over it from Asia into Greece. But when the bridge was finished, up came a great storm, and broke it to bits. Then Xerxes was angry with the sea.

"Whip it!" said Xerxes. And his men gave the sea three hundred lashes with a whip.

"Chain it!" said Xerxes. And they threw into the sea a pair of chains. For when King Xerxes was angry with men, he had them whipped and chained; so why not the sea?

While the sea was being whipped, he said to it: "You bad and bitter sea, your King punishes you for what you have done! And I will cross you, whether you will or no!"

Then he told his men to build a second bridge of ships, stronger than the first one. This time there was no storm, and the bridge held fast. But in case the sea should be angry as he crossed it, King Xerxes threw into it a golden bowl and a splendid sword as presents to make up for having whipped it.

Then King Xerxes and all his army marched over the bridge of ships into Greece.

KING XERXES AND THE SEA

King Xerxes saw the sea
Rise up and break his ships.
He tried to hold the sea in chains
And tame the sea with whips.

But when beneath his feet
The long green breakers rolled,
He tried to make the sea his friend,
And gave it gifts of gold.

King Xerxes and his pride
Are dust upon the ground;
No more he cracks his whip and throws
His golden gifts around.

And the sea he could not tame
Or bribe to do his will,
As it flowed three thousand years ago,
Is flowing, flowing still.

The Secret Path

ALL THE CITIES of Greece knew that King Xerxes of Persia was coming to conquer them. Before he came he sent his heralds to the different cities, and asked of each a little earth and a little water. If the cities gave him their earth and water he knew they would be his friends as he passed by, but if they sent him no earth and water he knew they would fight him on the way.

And there were rulers in Greece who feared him, and sent him the earth and water of their cities. But there were also brave men in Greece, who were not frightened of King Xerxes and his great army, and the bravest of them all was Leonidas, a King of Sparta. Of all the Greeks, the Spartans were the bravest and the hardest and the readiest to suffer pain and die.

Now Leonidas knew that when Xerxes came to

Greece he would have to cross over a great mountain by a narrow way that ran through it. The way was called Thermopylæ, or the Hot Gates, because at this place hot water came spouting out of the ground. There was no other way over the mountain except one—a secret path much higher up, that was known only to some of the Greeks themselves. Leonidas called to him all the soldiers from the different cities of Greece; some were ready to fight and die, but some were not. They were afraid of Xerxes, for Xerxes was coming with millions of men, and Leonidas had only four thousand. And of these just three hundred were Spartans. But Leonidas said:

"The Hot Gates are so narrow that only a very few men need stand in them at a time, and keep the army of Xerxes from coming through."

So there he waited with his Greeks for Xerxes, and he set a band of his soldiers to guard the secret path of which King Xerxes did not know.

When Xerxes marched up he could not believe that such a little army meant to fight with his great one. He camped on the plain below the mountain, and had a splendid throne built for himself to sit on while he watched the battle, and then he called

*He had a splendid throne built for
himself to sit on while he watched.*

one of his horsemen.

"Go and see what Leonidas is doing," said King Xerxes.

The horseman rode up the mountain, and then he rode down again.

"Well," said King Xerxes, "what did you see?"

"I saw the Spartans on guard in front of the wall," said the horseman.

"And what were they doing?" said Xerxes.

"O King, they were combing their hair."

Then Xerxes turned to a friend, who long ago had been a King of Sparta, and asked: "What does it mean when the Spartans comb their hair?"

"O King," said the friend, "whenever the Spartans comb their hair it means that they will fight with all their strength. They are the first men in Greece, and will be dangerous to you."

"Nonsense!" said Xerxes. "How can their little army fight my big one? I shall wait here a few days, and you'll see how they will lose heart and go away, and leave the mountain clear for me to pass through."

But four days went by, and the Greeks still guarded the Hot Gates. So on the fifth day Xerxes sent up his army of Persians to fight them; but the

Persians were killed in hundreds, and only a few Greeks fell." On the sixth day Xerxes said:

"I will send my Ten Thousand Immortals against them!"

But the Immortals did no better than the Persians, and many of them, too, were killed. As he watched the battle, and saw the soldiers of whom he was proudest being killed, King Xerxes leapt up three times from the throne where he sat, in terror and anger.

And the seventh day came, and once more the Persians attacked the Greeks, and were driven back.

Now as King Xerxes sat in his tent, wondering what he should do to get through the mountain, a little man came down to him from the Greeks and said he had a secret to sell.

"Who are you?" said Xerxes.

"I am a Greek," said the little man.

"What is your secret?" asked Xerxes.

Then the traitor said: "The Hot Gates are not the only way through the mountains. Higher up there is a secret path, and if you will pay me well I will show it to you."

Then Xerxes was delighted, and gave the traitor

a sum of gold, and when night came he led the King and his army up the mountain. The night was very still, but the mountains were covered with groves of oak, and the soft munching of the Persians sounded only like the rustling of the oak leaves; so that the Greeks who were set to guard the secret path did not know they were coming till they were very close. The Greeks were not prepared, and fled back into the mountains, leaving the path clear. Xerxes took no notice of them, but continued his march round the hills, to surprise Leonidas on the other side and in the night a Greek came running to Leonidas and cried:

"O Leonidas, we have been betrayed! The Persians have marched through the secret path, and at dawn will meet you in open battle!"

Then Leonidas said: "We cannot hope to win, so I and my three hundred Spartans will stay and die. Let all the rest go back to their cities in safety. In honor I must stay."

Then one of the leaders said: "Leonidas, my men will stay and die with you." And Leonidas thanked him, and the rest went away.

At sunrise the battle began. King Xerxes prayed

to the gods to help him, and then sent a big army of his roughest soldiers against the little band of Greeks. Behind Xerxes' army came the captains, driving on the men with whips. Many of Xerxes soldiers were trampled to death by those who came on behind. But Xerxes did not mind; he had more than enough soldiers to take their places again and again. The Greeks fought like lions, and thrust their enemies down over the mountain side into the sea; but at last the spears of the Greeks were all broken to bits, and then the Persians rushed on them and slew them. And Leonidas, the King of Sparta, was one of the first to die.

So Xerxes won the battle; but the honor belonged to Leonidas and his three hundred Spartans. And not long after this the Greeks met the Persians in their ships, and had a great battle on the sea at Salamis, and the Persians were defeated. And King Xerxes, who had crossed the sea, with his millions of men, in a galley with a golden sail, had to fly back to Persia alone, in a little boat rowed by one man.

LEONIDAS IS COMBING HIS HAIR

Leonidas is combing his hair.
King of Persia, beware, beware!

He has only a handful of men to spare,
So Leonidas is combing his hair.

They all must die in the mountain there,
But before they die they will do their share.

King of Persia, beware, beware—
Leonidas is combing his hair!

The King of Horses

A HUNDRED YEARS after King Xerxes had died in Persia, a Prince was born in Macedon on the other side of the sea. His name was Alexander, and he became one of the greatest Kings in the world. He was even a greater King than Xerxes. King Xerxes of Persia looked over the water at Greece and wanted to conquer it, but in spite of his big army he failed. King Alexander of Macedon looked over the water at Persia and wanted to conquer it, and he did not fail. Wherever he went he won the battles and the land, the cities and the people. King Xerxes wanted to conquer the world, and could not. But King Alexander conquered the world, and was not satisfied even then.

"Oh!" cried King Alexander, "I wish there were more worlds for me to conquer!"

Perhaps he looked up at the sky, thinking how he would like to conquer the stars, if he could march up his armies and take them. But even King Alexander could not do that.

When he was young and still only a Prince, he went with his father, Philip the King, to see the games and races, where all the best Greeks ran races on foot, and all the best horses ran chariot races. King Philip's horse won the chariot race, and King Philip was pleased and proud; then some one asked Prince Alexander, who was a quick runner:

"Would you not like to run in the foot race and win it?"

"Yes," said Prince Alexander, "if all the other men who ran were Kings!" And because there were no Kings to run with him, he would not run at all.

One day a man came from Thessaly to the court of King Philip; with him he had a horse, the most splendid ever seen.

"Will you buy him?" said the man to King Philip.

"How much do you want for him?" asked the King.

"His price is fifteen thousand dollars," said the man.

"What is his name?" said the King.

"His name is Bucephalus," said the man.

"Well," said the King, "we will take him into the field and try him."

The King and all his courtiers led the way to the field, and Prince Alexander went too; and the man of Thessaly led in Bucephalus, and the King sent for his grooms to ride him round the sunny field. But Bucephalus was full of temper; his temper was as strong as his beautiful body. When the grooms came near him he stamped and he snorted, and lashed his tail; he reared on his hind legs, and rolled his eyes at the grooms. They were used to horses, and clever with them; but even the cleverest could not come near Bucephalus. He was the fiercest horse they had ever seen. And as he pranced at them in the air, his great black shadow pranced also on the grass, with kicking hoofs and flying mane.

Then King Philip got angry, and said to the man of Thessaly:

"Take your horse away! Why did you bring a wild beast for sale?"

*All this time Prince Alexander
had been watching the horse.*

Now all this time Prince Alexander had been watching the horse, and he loved it for its beauty and strength and fiery spirit. He was a Prince who wished only to race with Kings, and Bucephalus seemed to him the very king of horses. So when he heard his father's words he cried:

"Oh, what a horse we are losing, because none of these grooms has the spirit to manage him!"

King Philip frowned, and said: "Young man, you talk as though you knew more than your elders, and could ride the horse yourself."

"And so I could!" cried Alexander.

"Well," said King Philip, "you may try; but if you fail what forfeit will you pay?"

"I will pay fifteen thousand dollars, the price of the horse," said Alexander.

Then all the courtiers laughed aloud, and the King agreed.

Alexander ran to Bucephalus, and Bucephalus let him come nearer. Perhaps he, who was the king of horses, knew in his heart that Alexander was a king of men. So he allowed Alexander to take hold of his bridle. Now Bucephalus was standing with his back to the sun, so that his great shadow lay in front of him, and Alexander had seen how the shadow pranced and kicked like a big black horse on the ground. He said to himself:

"The sight of his own wild shadow has frightened Bucephalus." And very gently he turned the horse with its face to the sun, so that the shadow fell behind him, and Bucephalus could not see it. But still Bucephalus snorted and trembled with excitement, and Alexander stood by him, stroking his neck and speaking softly to him. The quiet touch and words calmed the horse, and at last he stood still. Then Alexander let fall his mantle, sprang lightly on the horse's back, and set him going. And Bucephalus knew suddenly that his master was on his back, who would be proud of his strength and his speed; and he put down his head and ran round the field like the wind.

At first King Philip and his court were terrified when they saw the young Prince going at such great speed on the horse's back; but when Alexander had raced around the field and brought Bucephalus to a standstill in front of his father, all the people cheered and shouted, and Philip wept for joy, and kissed him, saying:

"Oh, my son, you must find a greater country

than mine to rule! The kingdom of Macedon is too small for you!"

And he gave Bucephalus to Alexander for his own, and sent for the wisest man in all Greece to be his teacher. And the wise man, whose name was Aristotle, read with him the tale of Troy, and young Alexander loved it more than all other tales, and dreamed of the day when he should become like the heroes in that tale, as brave as Achilles, as strong as Ajax, and as wise as Ulysses.

ALEXANDER TO HIS HORSE

Quiet, my horse, be quiet,
In the sunny meadow!
Shall your great heart riot
For terror of a shadow?

Oh, you are king of horses,
And king of men am I;
And we will take our courses
Together by and by.

We two will ride the meadows
Of all the world again—
We will not fight with shadows,
But men, my horse, with men!

Alexander the King

KING PHILIP OF Macedon died, and Prince Alexander became King. He was only twenty years old, and they called him Alexander the Great.

When he was a boy he dreamed of crossing the water to see Troy, where Achilles had fought; and then to conquer Persia, whose King, Xerxes, had tried to conquer Greece a hundred years ago. The King of Persia was now called Darius, and he prepared an army for Alexander's coming; he too was a mighty King.

As soon as Alexander had crossed the sea, he went to Troy, where Achilles was buried hundreds of years ago; and Alexander poured oil on his tomb, and ran around it with his friends, to do it honor, for that was the custom. Then he rode on, at the head of his army, to meet the army of King Darius, which was waiting for him on the other side of a river.

It was late in the day when they got to the river, and Alexander, eager for the fight, wanted to cross at once. But a friend laid his hand on his arm and said:

"It is too late today; and see how deep the river is, and how rough the banks are."

Alexander flung back his head, and cried: "We have just crossed the sea; and the sea itself would be ashamed of us if we could not cross the river!" So saying, he rushed into the river on his horse, with his horsemen behind him.

The further bank was lined with the Persian horsemen and bowmen, and they shot their arrows like rain at Alexander and his men; and the river ran so fast that it often swept him away, and it ran so high that its waves ran over his head, and the enemy thought:

"Is this the great King Alexander? He must be mad to come to us so!"

But still Alexander rode on through the water and still his horsemen followed him; and they pushed their way up the bank where the Persians were waiting for them. Then the Persian horsemen met the horsemen of Alexander, and soon there was a great confusion of men and horses, and clashing swords, and waving battle-axes; and wherever Alexander was seen the Persians fought fiercest, hoping to kill him. He was easy to see, for on each side of his shield and his helmet there was a large and beautiful plume of white feathers. But Alexander fought like Achilles himself; and though his horse was killed under him, he was not hurt. The horse was not his beautiful Bucephalus, but another one. He fought so fiercely that at last the Persians turned and fled away, and the battle was over. Alexander had won his first battle in Asia.

But Alexander could not rest. He marched on with his army, conquering all the countries and the cities in his way, for he longed to meet with King Darius himself, and take the King's city. Darius, too, was eager to fight Alexander and set out with his army to meet him; but in the night they wandered different ways and missed each other. Then Darius turned round and tried to get back to his camp, but on the way Alexander caught him in a narrow place, with the sea on one side and the mountains on the other, and the second big battle took place.

In this battle King Darius met King Alexander face to face, and wounded him a little. But in spite of this Alexander won the battle, and the Persians were beaten for the second time, and fled away again. And Alexander marched onto the camp of Darius, where he had left his wife, his mother, and his daughters, and heaps of treasure: fine clothes, rich furniture, and chests of gold and silver. Alexander looked round upon all the riches and said:

"This is what it is to be a King!" And he sat down at a table and told his men to treat the women kindly, and gave orders what was to be done with the treasure. As he was looking at the costly things, they brought him a beautiful casket they had found, and of all the treasures it was the richest and rarest.

"I will have this for myself," said Alexander. "And now tell me, my friends, what do you think I ought to keep in such a beautiful casket ?"

Some said one thing, and some another; some said clothes, and some said jewels. But Alexander shook his head.

"No," he said, "there is only one thing good enough for such a casket—the book with the Tale of Troy in it."

And he put the book in the casket, and always kept there the tale of the great Achilles whom he loved.

But still Alexander could not rest. He wanted to meet Darius again and conquer him for good and all. And at last he found him at a place called the House of the Dromedary, because once an ancient King of Persia had escaped from his enemies on a dromedary's back, and afterwards he gave the dromedary that place to live in, and made the near-by villages feed her and honor her till she died.

Here it was that Alexander came on the Persians for the third time. In the night his friend said to him:

"The whole plain over there is covered with our enemies; their torches are flaming, and they are howling in the camp like the bellowing of the sea. Take my advice, and attack them in the night, when darkness will hide your coming."

But Alexander looked at him and said: "I will not steal a victory." For he was too proud to do anything but meet his enemy in the daylight. And he went into his tent and slept soundly, though the greatest battle in the world was to take place the next day.

The next morning he rode out to battle in a helmet that shone like silver, and a collar set with precious stones, and a sword of fine steel that had been given him by a King, and a belt that was more gorgeous than all the rest of his armor. And as he rode with his men behind him, an eagle appeared in the sky, and flew over his head, leading him on to the Persians. At the sight of it his horsemen shouted aloud, and their horses galloped like a torrent of water pouring down the mountain. The Persians gave way before them at once, and they galloped on towards the spot where King Darius stood up in his chariot, so tall and so handsome, surrounded by his guard. But Alexander seemed still more tall and terrible as he came on, and the Persian guards were filled with fear and turned to fly; and King Darius found himself alone, with his men falling around him or running away. So then he leapt down from his chariot, and sprang on the back of a mare standing by, and rode away over the plain and escaped.

And so ended the third battle, and all Persia now belonged to Alexander; and he marched on with his men to the King of Persia's city, and on the way found so much treasure that it took twenty thousand

An eagle appeared in the sky,
and flew over his head, leading him on.

mules and five thousand camels to carry it.

When he came into the King's city, the first thing Alexander saw was a great statue of the ancient King Xerxes, lying in the streets where it had fallen when the people ran away. And Alexander stood and looked at the statue of the King who had once tried to conquer Greece, thinking, "Shall I stand it up again, or shall I let it lie?" But the power of Persia had fallen, so he let it lie. He went into the palace of the Persian Kings, and sat on the throne under a golden canopy, and made a great feast for all his friends that night. And when the feast was ended he sprang up from the throne with his garland on his head and a torch in his hand; and all his friends with garlands and torches followed him dancing out of the palace, and spread themselves about it and set it alight at all points. And the palace of the great Kings of Persia flared up in the night; and in the morning it was only a heap of ashes.

THE TWO EAGLES

When Alexander went to war,
How bright the morning shone!
Lo, in the golden dawn and blue
An eagle out of heaven flew,
And led his army on.

When Alexander went to war,
He said: "They know my worth!
An eagle in the heavens, see,
Appears to show the way to me,
The Eagle of the earth!"

The Children of the Wolf

IN THE CITY of Alba, in the lovely land of Italy, Æneas was King. He had been a Prince in Troy, and when Troy was burned he sailed away to Italy with his men and his ships full of treasure. And when he came to Italy he married the King's daughter, and their sons became the Kings of Alba after them.

Now it happened that when the thirteenth King of Alba died, he left behind him two sons whose names were Amulius and Numitor, and they could not decide which of the two should be King. So Amulius said to Numitor:

"Let us divide what we have. Here, on the one hand, is the city and the land; and here, on the other, is all the treasure that Æneas brought to Italy from Troy, hundreds of years ago. Which will you have, Numitor—the treasure or the land?"

"I will choose the land,' said Numitor, "and you shall keep the treasure. You will be a richer man than I, but I will be the King of the land."

Amulius agreed to this, and the division was made. But Amulius longed for the land as well as the treasure, and he was now a rich man, while Numitor was only a poor King. So with his money Amulius paid the soldiers to fight for him, and he turned Numitor out of the city and became the King of Alba. In this way he had the money and the land as well.

Numitor went away with his friends and lived outside the city, keeping his cows and sheep like a poor man, as he now was. But he could not take with him his daughter Sylvia, for her uncle Amulius kept her a prisoner in the city. Amulius also had a beautiful daughter, named Antho, who loved her cousin Sylvia dearly.

One day an old servant came to King Amulius and said:

"O King, there is danger to you. For the Princess Sylvia has twin babies, both boys, and who knows what they will not do to you when they are men?"

Then King Amulius was frightened, and said:

"Sylvia and her sons must be put to death."

But the Princess Antho fell on her knees before him and begged for Sylvia's life. "Do not kill her, father," she said, "for I love her."

She begged so hard that Amulius gave way.

"Well, Sylvia shall live," said he, "but the babies must die."

And he told his servant to take the babies away in a little trough, and cast them into the river Tiber.

The servant did as he was told—but when he got to the Tiber it was running high, with so strong a current that he was afraid to go near it. So he laid the trough as close as he could to the water, thinking, "The river will rise and drown the children, or they will die of cold and hunger." And he went away.

The water in the river rose higher and higher, and came over the banks to where the trough was lying; but instead of drowning the babies, it lifted the trough as gently as though it were a mother rocking a cradle, and floated it away down the river, and brought it to shore in a pleasant grove. There it left the trough under a great fig tree, and flowed on while the children slept.

As they lay there, a tap-tap-tap was heard on the

bark of the fig tree, and a woodpecker settled in the leaves and looked down on the children. And then a soft pad-pad-pad was heard in the woods, and through the trees came a big gray mother wolf, and she too stood over the trough and looked down at the children. "What lovely little cubs they are!" thought the wolf; and the woodpecker sang: "What lovely little birds!"

Then the two children woke, and were hungry, and seeing the wolf above them, they reached up their little hands and mouths as though she had been their own mother and they her cubs. And the woodpecker flew away into the woods to find berries for them to eat, and she too fed them as though they had been her own nestlings. So for a time the two babies were cared for by the wolf and the woodpecker, and they became strong and rosy babies, and did not care whether they were boys or birds or little cubs.

Then one day an old man, one of Amulius's herdsmen, came by, and he found the two children and the trough under the fig tree. They were far away from the city of Alba, but he had heard all the tale of the Princess Sylvia's two sons, and he knew who the babies were. His heart was full of

"What lovely little cubs they are!" thought the wolf.

pity, and he took them away to his own hut. There he gave them the names of Romulus and Remus, and brought them up as though they were peasants like himself. But they did not look like peasants; they grew up tall and strong and beautiful, and carried themselves like Kings. But they were also wild and rough, from living in the woods, and when they were young men they went about the countryside with the herdsmen of King Amulius, looking after the cattle.

Now not far away lived their own grandfather, Numitor, with his servants who looked after his cattle; and one day there was a quarrel between the servants of Numitor and the servants of Amulius, who had tried to steal each other's cows. In the quarrel Remus was taken prisoner, and was brought before his grandfather Numitor, who had never set eyes on him till then. And he was so tall and strong and kingly in his bearing that Numitor thought: "This boy cannot be a peasant." And he asked him who he was.

"I do not know who I am," said Remus. "I and my brother Romulus have been brought up by the herdsman as though we were his sons; but we do not feel like his sons, and we know that there is some secret about our birth."

Then he told Numitor the tale of the trough and the wolf and the woodpecker, and said that the herdsman still had the trough to prove the truth of the tale. And Numitor was overjoyed, and said: "You and your brother Romulus are my own grandsons, and your mother is my daughter Sylvia, whom Amulius keeps in prison." And he embraced Remus.

And now a great noise was heard, for Romulus, hearing that Remus had been taken had gathered a company of men to come and save him. But when he saw his brother in Numitor's arms, and heard that he and Remus were the grandsons of a King, he went with all his men to Alba, where Amulius was still King. And he attacked the palace, and killed Amulius, and set his mother free.

Then he went back to Numitor and said:

"Grandfather, you must now come and be King of Alba, as you should always have been. But as for me and Remus, we will go a little further off and build another city, which we will rule."

So this was done, and Romulus and Remus went to the hills eighteen miles away to build the city of Rome. When it came to the building of the city, however, the two brothers quarreled, just as Numitor and Amulius had quarreled long ago; for Remus said the city should be built on one hill, but Romulus said it should be built on another, and each wanted to have his way. Then Romulus and his friends marked out a great square on the ground, on which the walls of Rome were to be built, and when the square was marked they began to dig in it and make a ditch.

And Remus came up and watched them, very angry, and mocked at their work and tried to prevent it.

"Are these the walls of Rome?" cried Remus. "Why, the enemy will leap over them like this!" And as he spoke he jumped over the ditch into the midst of the workmen.

Then one of the men sprang up and cried:

"And the men of Rome will drive them back like this!" And he struck a great blow at Remus, who fell down dead.

And the workman, seeing what he had done, fled far away as fast as he could, but Romulus cried out with grief, and was so unhappy that he tried to kill himself too. However, his friends stopped him.

And so Romulus had to build the city of Rome alone. And into the ditch, before the walls were built, the men threw a little of everything good that grew in the land: olives, and corn, and grapes, and flowers. Then each man brought a handful of earth from his own part of Italy, and threw that in too. So the city walls of Rome were built upon the best of everything that was in Italy, and Rome became the greatest city in the land, and then the greatest city in the world. And Romulus was its first King.

Two Little Boys

Said old Father Tiber, a-wandering by,
"Two little fish on my river banks lie."

Said young Mrs. Woodpecker, perched in the tree,
"Two little birds in the bushes I see."

Said gray Mother Wolf, as she bent down her head,
"Two little cubs that have got to be fed."

Said the kind old Herdsman, on hearing the noise,
"Romulus! Remus! Two fine little boys!"

The Man with the Name of a City

ROME WAS THE proudest city in the world, and
Caius Marcius the proudest man in Rome. He was
the son of a nobleman, but when he was a little
boy his father died, and his mother brought him
up, and she was as full of spirit as a man.

With such a mother, he grew up proud and
fierce; his arm was as strong as a thunderbolt, his
voice was as loud as thunder, and his temper was
like a storm. When he went into battle he always
fought where there was most danger, and he won
the battles, and came home with the victor's
crown of oak leaves on his head and many
wounds on his body. His mother was as proud of
his wounds as of his crown, and praised him for
them. But Caius Marcius did not like to hear
himself praised. He wanted to fight battles and
win them, but he did not want to hear them talked

about. He loved Rome, and wanted her to be the greatest city in the world, but he did not love the people of Rome. He was so proud that he thought himself above the common people, because he was a nobleman, and the people knew it. So in their hearts they did not love him either, though with their tongues they often praised him for fighting so bravely, and saving Rome from her enemies.

The greatest enemy of Rome was a soldier called Tullus. He lived in Antium, on the shores of the sea, and his people were the Volscians. Many times Caius Marcius went out with the Roman army to fight the Volscians, and one day, in a great battle, he took one of their cities, called Corioli, almost by himself. He had only a very few men with him. The Roman general gave him his own horse as a reward, and told him to choose a tenth part of all the treasure they had taken from the Volscians.

But Caius Marcius said:

"I will not take any of the treasure, because I fight for honor, and not for riches."

"Then," said the general, "since you alone took the city of Corioli, we will give you in honor the name of Coriolanus, and your deed will always be remembered when men speak your name."

So Caius Marcius came out of that battle with a new horse and a new name. After that, people always called him Coriolanus.

The Romans made peace with the Volscians, and the war was over. But now Rome was full of her own quarrels, like a family that quarrels among itself. For the common people did not like the noblemen, and wanted more power, and chose leaders to speak for them. And the noblemen did not like the common people, and they feared their new power. But nobody hated the people so much as the proud Coriolanus.

Now the times in Rome were hard, corn was scarce, and the people were hungry. But a King who lived in Sicily sent a great present of corn to the city, and the noblemen said:

"Let us give some of the corn to the people for nothing, and let us sell the rest to them as cheap as we can."

But Coriolanus said to the other noblemen: "You will be fools if you do this. The people will think you do it because you are afraid of them; and they will be twice as rude as before and more powerful than ever." And the people heard what he had said, and were furious with Coriolanus for keeping the corn from them.

Soon after this Coriolanus wanted to be chosen for one of the rulers of Rome, and the noblemen were willing, but no man could be chosen for a ruler unless the people also chose him. Any one who wished for the people's goodwill had to put off his rich robes and stand in the market place in a humble gown, and show his wounds to the people, telling them what he had done for Rome, and asking them to choose him. When Coriolanus heard that he too must do this, all his pride rose up like a storm. What! must *he* put on a humble dress? Must *he* show his wounds and talk of his own battles? Must *he* beg of the people, whom he despised so much? Still, if he wished to be ruler, it had to be done.

Much against his will, the proud Coriolanus stood in the market place, and begged of the people. And the people looked at his wounds, and remembered how he had fought for Rome, and promised to choose him. But the leaders of the people went among them and said: "Will you choose a man who hates you so much that he will not let you have cheap corn when you are hungry?" Then the people changed their minds again, and on the day when the ruler had to be chosen, they chose another man. And the anger of Coriolanus broke out against them like a flame, and their anger broke out against him; and the people came together, and with one voice cried that Coriolanus must leave the city of Rome and never come back again.

Then Coriolanus went out through one of the gates of Rome, and his heart was filled with thoughts of anger against the people. So he disguised himself like a beggar and went away to Antium, on the shores of the sea, where lived his old enemy Tullus, the general of the Volscians. He came into the hall where Tullus sat at his banquet, and Tullus said:

"Who are you?"

Coriolanus dropped his cloak and said:

"I am your enemy, Caius Marcius Coriolanus. I have often fought against you, but Rome is ungrateful, and has turned me out of her gates. Now, if you like, I will fight for you and lead your army against Rome."

Tullus was full of joy and said: "My old enemy,

you have brought us a priceless gift—yourself; and you shall lead the Volscians against Rome."

So Coriolanus, at the head of the Volscian army, began to make war on the country outside Rome, coming nearer and nearer to Rome itself. News of his battles and victories came into the city, and the Romans were full of fear, because Coriolanus, who had fought so splendidly for them of old, was now fighting against them. And even the people were sorry for what they had done, and wanted to have him back again. So some of the chief men of Rome went out of the city to find Coriolanus, in the Volscian camp, and beg him to put an end to the wars and come back to Rome. They found him sitting in high state among the Volscians, and he looked sterner than they had ever seen him. They spoke humbly to him, putting their request. But he answered them bitterly, saying:

"You have cast me out of Rome. Now I am the general of the Volscians, and I say you must give back to the Volscians all you took from them in the early wars, otherwise the war must go on."

Then the Romans went back, and sent out the priests of Rome to beg Coriolanus to make peace with the city; but he was as stern as ever, and answered the priests: "If you do not accept my demands, the war must go on." And the priests went back, and sent out the women.

When Coriolanus saw all the women in Rome coming out through the gates to beg him to make peace, he tried to look sterner than ever. But when he saw that the women were led by his own mother and his dear wife he could be proud no longer. He jumped down from his seat and ran to meet them, and embraced them both. And then his wife and his mother knelt at his feet and begged him to save Rome.

Coriolanus cried out: "O mother, what have you done?" And he raised her tenderly from the ground and said: "You have saved Rome, but you have ruined me." And he told them to go back and say that the women had saved the city.

Then the women returned to Rome, and Coriolanus marched away to Antium with the Volscians. And all Rome rejoiced, and threw open the temples, and the people went in with flowers on their heads to give thanks for being saved. And they built a beautiful temple in honor of the women of Rome.

But far away, in Antium, on the shores of the

sea, Tullus turned in anger upon Coriolanus, his old enemy, crying out that he was a traitor to the Volscians, because he had spared Rome. And his friends rushed upon Coriolanus in a body and killed him on the spot; and no one that was present lifted a hand to save him.

THE PROUDEST ROMAN

The proudest Roman of them all,
Whose temper like a flame did leap,
When saw his mother fall
Upon her aged knees and weep,
He knew she could not be denied,
    And laid aside
    His Roman pride.

She saved her town, but killed her son—
When mothers kneel, all pride is vain.
"Mother," he said, "what have you done?"
And stooped and raised her up again.
"Go home to Rome all safe," said he,
    "Let fall on me
    What has to be."

Hannibal with the One Eye

WHEN THE CITY of Rome was built, she was like a little wave rising up among the other waves of the sea. But as the years rolled on the power of Rome rose up bigger and bigger, like a little wave growing into a great wave, higher and stronger than all the other waves in the sea. The other cities in the world, that were like the little waves, knew that she was greater than they were, and many of them feared her and wished to destroy her before she swallowed them up. And the city of Carthage in Africa feared and hated her most. Many battles took place between the Romans and the dark-skinned men of Carthage, and the Romans were the victors.

Then one day a little dark boy was born in Carthage, called Hannibal. When he was nine years old his father, Hamilcar, made ready to lead the men of Carthage into battle, for he was a great

general. The little Hannibal said to his father:
"Take me too!"

And the big Hamilcar looked down upon the little Hannibal and thought: "One day he will be big enough to fight the Romans." And he took Hannibal into the temple and told him to lay his hand on the altar.

"Now," said Hamilcar, "swear to be the enemy of Rome all your life."

And Hannibal swore the oath. When he grew up he never forgot it. He was the greatest general in Carthage, and the greatest enemy Rome ever had. He had only one eye, but he saw farther with it than most men see with two.

He got together a great army of men with black skins and brown; he got horses and elephants too, and sailed away from Carthage to fight Rome. And Rome heard that he was coming to take her and prepared herself, for she knew that Hannibal was one of the greatest generals in the world.

Before he could get to Rome, Hannibal had to march through Spain, and on the way many Spaniards joined his army. So now he had black men and brown men, and horses and elephants, and Spaniards in white tunics with purple borders.

And before he could get to Rome, Hannibal had to march through Gaul, and the Gauls also flocked to join his army. And now he had black men and brown men, and horses and elephants, and Spaniards in white and purple tunics, and Gauls who fought half naked, like wild men as they were.

And before he could get to Rome, Hannibal had to cross the Alps. Oh, those great mountains, with their snowy tops and cold white mists! Hannibal was not used to such mountains in his burning hot country in Africa. And it seemed harder to cross the tall, icy mountains than to fight battles.

Yet over the Alps he went with his army, his black men and brown men, his horses and elephants, his white and purple Spaniards, and his wild, naked Gauls. Their way was full of danger and hardships. They met savages who fought with them, and snowstorms that blinded them, and icy winds that froze them, and mists in which they were lost. But in fifteen days Hannibal got his great army over the Alps. And Rome heard he was coming, and sent out her army under two generals, Fabius and Minucius.

Now Minucius was young and brave and rash, and Fabius was old and wise and patient. Minucius said: "Let us attack Hannibal in a great battle!" But Fabius said: "No, let us lie in wait in the mountains, and not come to open battle with him. For if we just hold him in check amongst the hills and valleys which we know so well, and which are strange to him, at last he will be tired out."

Minucius hated this advice, but for a time let Fabius have his way. And Hannibal could not draw the Roman army into open fight. His army was on one hill, and theirs on another. When he showed himself on his hill, they showed themselves on theirs; when he moved on towards them, they disappeared and moved a little away; and by no means could Hannibal meet them and fight them.

Then he thought of a strange trick to drive the Romans off their hill. In the night he got two thousand oxen, and fastened great flaming torches on their horns; and he sent a few men to drive them up the hill. At first the oxen went softly up the hill, with their torches burning steadily on their heads; and from all the hills around the shepherds and herdsmen looked down in wonder at what they thought was a great army, carrying flaming torches through the night. But presently the torches burnt down to the roots of their horns, and the oxen felt the fire and became mad with pain, and they rushed up the mountain with flaming foreheads and tails, scattering fire on all sides. And the Romans on the hill were terrified and marched away, and Hannibal came up and took the hill from which he had driven the Romans out.

When the Romans found out the trick, they were all angry with the old patient Fabius who had not let them fight Hannibal, and Minucius said: "You see, Fabius, how useless all your wisdom was!" And the old Fabius was in disgrace at Rome, and Minucius was allowed to have his way with his half of the army.

Minucius marched out with his men to meet Hannibal in open battle; but Hannibal knew he was coming, and had hidden bands of men in the ditches and the hollows of the land. Then with the rest of his men he met Minucius, and as they were fighting, the black men rose up from the ditches and surrounded Minucius on all sides.

Fabius saw it all from the camp, and he cried to his half of the army:

"Now, my brave soldiers, let us help Minucius with all our strength, for he loves Rome and is a brave man, and this is not the hour to blame him for his mistakes." And Fabius led on his men as though he were a young man, and not an old one; and he pushed his way through Hannibal's black troops, and saved Minucius, and Hannibal had to fall back. And as his men fell back, Hannibal pointed to the old wise Fabius and said to his friends: "Look! there is the cloud full of thunder which has burst upon us from the mountains."

So Fabius saved, not only Minucius, but Rome, from Hannibal, for, some time after this battle, Hannibal had to return to Carthage, which was being attacked by another army of Romans who had sailed over the sea. And in his own country Hannibal was defeated, and had to fly away and take refuge with a King in a foreign country. The Romans demanded of the King that he should give Hannibal up to them. But Hannibal, who was now an old man, took from his finger a golden ring, in which a strong poison was hidden; and rather than fall into the hands of the Romans, against whom he had sworn his oath as a little boy, he drank the poison.

So died the greatest enemy of Rome, and the power of Rome still grew.

WHEN HANNIBAL CROSSED THE ALPS

Hannibal crossed the Alps!
Hannibal crossed the Alps!
    With his black men,
    His brown men,
    His countrymen,
    His townmen.
With his Gauls, and his Spaniards, his
    horses and elephants,
Hannibal crossed the Alps!

Hannibal crossed the Alps!
Hannibal crossed the Alps!
    For his bowmen,
    His spearmen,
    His front men,
    His rear men,
His Gauls and his Spaniards, his horses
    and elephants,
Wanted the Roman scalps!
And *that's* why Hannibal, Hannibal,
    Hannibal,
Hannibal crossed the Alps!

The Roads of Rome

AT LAST A MAN was born who loved Rome better than any of her other sons. His name was Julius Cæsar. There had been Romans who were proud of Rome, and fought battles for her and brought back riches. When they went out to the other countries of the earth, they killed in thousands the enemies they fought, and destroyed their cities, and left all things in ruin.

But Julius Cæsar loved Rome in a better way than that. He, too, was a great soldier, and went out to fight Rome's battles, and take the cities that were her enemies. But he saw how glorious a city his Rome was, how well she was managed, and how much happier and better off the people of Rome were than the wild, savage people he went out to fight. And he knew that this was because wise men had thought out what was best for

Rome, and kept all things in order. So Julius Cæsar said to himself:

"I also will go all over the world with my armies, and fight Rome's enemies. But when I have conquered them I will not kill them and pull their cities down. No, wherever I go I will leave Romans behind me, who will teach our enemies how to live well and order their cities better. In the rough lands where there are no roads we will teach them how to make fine, broad roads like the Roman roads, so that all over the world the people can go easily to and fro. So there shall be not only one Rome, but many little Romes, spread over the world; and all the great roads we make wherever we go shall lead back from the little cities to Rome herself!"

This was the dream and the desire of Julius Cæsar.

Then Cæsar asked Rome to give him armies, and Rome gave him many legions of men, and he went forth. For many years he lived in France and Spain, which were savage lands then, and he did all he meant to do. He fought the wild people, and when he had conquered them he taught them how to build up their cities and order them well, and make the great roads of the world. Between his battles he read the life of the great Alexander, whom he admired; but once he wept while reading, because Alexander seemed a greater man than he himself was, and he wished to be like him, just as Alexander once used to read of the great Achilles and wish to be like him. Yet, in the end, Julius Cæsar was a greater man than either Alexander or Achilles.

In ten years he had taken eight hundred cities and conquered three hundred nations, yet it was not because of this alone that he was great. It was because of his dream of leaving all the cities and nations better than he had found them. All over the world went Cæsar with his legions of soldiers. They would have followed him anywhere. Sometimes they fought for him when they were starving, eating only the roots in the fields, and giving their horses seaweed from the shore, rather than turn back.

Then one day Cæsar heard talk of a little island over the sea, not far from France. Nobody knew much about it. Some men even said it was a fable and a fairy tale, there was no such island at all. Others said yes, it was a true island, and full of savages who did not know how to live.

So Cæsar followed his dream once more, and got ships, and sailed over the sea to find the island; and it was indeed a true island, and no fable, for it was the island of Britain—now called England—a land full of swamps and savages and few cities and no roads.

Here once more Cæsar fought his battles, and when he sailed away he left behind him many Romans who taught the Britons how to build and make roads, some of the very roads the English people walk on today. But the houses the Romans built have fallen or been buried under the earth. Only here and there in England still a plowman in a field will sometimes strike something hard under the earth, and deep down he will find the floor of some old Roman house, laid out in lovely pictures made of colored stones.

At last Cæsar came back to Rome, and was the first man in the city. And now his dream was to put things in Rome in still better order than he found them. The very days of the Calendar were out of order, and did not fall right with the seasons of the year; and it was Cæsar who put them right, and made the days and weeks and months as we now know them.

But there were still people in Rome who feared Cæsar's power, and thought that now he was so great he might want to be King. It was then a rule that there should be no Kings in Rome, and Cæsar's enemies said among themselves: "If he tries to become King, he must die."

Now there was a great holiday in Rome, and Cæsar came out to see it; and he wore a purple robe and sat on a golden chair, in sight of all the people. As he sat there, his best friend, Antony came up and offered him a laurel wreath like a crown; but Cæsar refused to take it, and the people clapped their hands. Then once more Antony offered the crown to Cæsar, and the people were silent; for even they did not want Cæsar to be King, because of the rule. So once more Cæsar refused it, and then the people shouted.

But Cæsar's enemies said among themselves: "Cæsar himself arranged this, to try whether the people would let him be King or no; and though he pretends to refuse the crown, in his heart he really wants it." And they made this the excuse, a little later, to fall upon him and kill him.

So the man who had done most for Rome was killed by the Romans themselves. And nobody knows, if he had lived, whether he would have become King or no. But we do know that the roads he made still march over the face of the earth, and the days still march through the year as he ordered them.

GOOD ORDER

Cæsar looked over his armies
  And spoke to his legions ten:
"Wash with care, and comb your hair,
And mind your step in the Left Wing there.
And keep yourselves in good order!"
  Cæsar said to his men.

Cæsar looked over the marshlands
  And brought the big roads to birth;
"See they are neat and clean and sweet,
That men may travel with easy feet,
And keep yourself in good order!"
  Cæsar said to the earth.

Cæsar looked over the Calendar,
  As muddled as any maze.
"Here's winter's moon in the middle of June!
Watch the seasons and change your tune,
And keep the year in good order!"
  Cæsar said to the days.

Part II

From Beowulf to William the Conqueror

To Hilda's
Barbara

Grendel the Monster

IT CAME INTO the mind of King Hrothgar that he would build a great hall in his kingdom of Denmark, a greater hall than any man had ever built before. And when it was built he called it Heorot. High in the air rose the roof of Heorot, and so strong were the walls that it seemed as though nothing but fire could ever destroy them.

Then King Hrothgar made a great banquet for his people, and to all who came he gave golden rings.

Now outside the hall in the dark forest lived a dreadful monster called Grendel, a creature who was part man and part beast. The sound of the laughter in Heorot made him wild, and he hated the song of the minstrel. So when night fell he crept to the hall, and there he saw Hrothgar's men sleeping after the feast. Straightway Grendel seized thirty of the sleepers, and fled yelling back to his forest, where he devoured them.

Next morning there was weeping and wailing in Heorot, and in the night the monster Grendel came again, and devoured even more of those who slept there. For twelve years he continued to come by night to the hall of Hrothgar, and to the houses of all his friends, doing them dreadful harm. The tale of it went into distant lands, and came at last to the ears of Hygelac, King of the Goths, and of Beowulf his young kinsman.

Now Beowulf was a great hero, and had the strength of thirty men.

He ordered a swift boat to be prepared, and took fourteen of his friends with him, to help him rid Hrothgar of Grendel the monster. Over the foamy sea the ship went like a bird, and at last came in sight of a land of shining cliffs and towering hills, and headlands running out into the waves. Eagerly Beowulf landed with his fourteen Goths, and they ran down the hill till they came to the glorious hall, of which they had often heard. For no king in the world had so famous a hall as Heorot. At the door of the hall stood King Hrothgar's herald, who said:

"Whence come you tall bold fellows, with your shields, helmets and spears? And who are you?"

"My name is Beowulf," said he. "Take me to your King, and I will tell him why I come."

Then Beowulf was taken in to Hrothgar, and the hero said to the King:

"Hail, Hrothgar! I am kinsman to Hygelac, King of the Goths, and young as I am, I have undertaken many deeds and seen much danger. And now I am come to fight the monster Grendel single-handed."

Then King Hrothgar rejoiced, and answered:

"Beowulf, my friend, tonight you shall keep guard in the hall where Grendel has done so many terrible things. But first sit down and share our feast with us."

A table was cleared for Beowulf and the Goths, and there they sat and ate with the Danes, and the men sang jovial songs together.

Then Hrothgar's Queen came in her gold array, bearing a great jeweled cup full of mead in her hands. She offered it in turn to all the men, first to the King, and last to Beowulf. While the hero drank, she spoke words of thanks and praise for his coming. And Beowulf said:

Then through the night came Grendel.

"As I sat in my boat I vowed to myself to free you from the monster, or die in the struggle."

The words of the hero made the Queen glad. Then in her gold array she went and sat by the King.

The feast came to an end, the King and Queen departed with the Danes, and Beowulf and the Goths lay down in the hall. But first Beowulf took off his armor, saying:

"Since Grendel the Monster fights only with his naked strength, so will I."

Soon the Goths, who should have guarded the hall were sleeping—all but one. Beowulf waked and watched.

Then through the night came Grendel, tearing along in his fury to the hall to get his supper of men. The iron-barred doors sprang open at his touch, and there on the paved floor he saw the sleeping Goths. His fury turned to laughter at the sight, and before Beowulf could stop him he had seized the nearest sleeper and devoured him.

The next he came to was Beowulf himself. He reached out his great arm like a fang, but Beowulf gripped the arm before it could clutch him. At that mighty grip, Grendel knew that he had met the strongest man in the world.

Now the monster was full of fear, and tried to get away. But Beowulf grappled with him, and would not let him go. Up and down, to and fro, raged Grendel, but he could not get free from Beowulf's grip. The hall was filled with roaring, the sides and roof shook with the struggles of the hero and the monster. The seats were torn up, the golden walls destroyed, and in the distance the Danes heard the great noise and trembled in their beds.

At last Grendel got his death wound. With a mighty tug Beowulf pulled the arm clean out of the monster's shoulder. Grendel gave one last howl, and fled back to his forest to die, and Beowulf fixed the arm in the roof of the hall as a sign that all danger from Grendel was past.

By the light of the morning the King came with his lords and the Queen with her ladies along the path to the hall. When Hrothgar saw the arm in the roof, he said:

"Beowulf, I will love you forever like my own son for the deeds you have done."

"I wish, all the same," said Beowulf, "that you could have seen the monster himself. However, there is his arm."

Then men and women came to make Heorot

new and lovely. They mended the wrecked walls and seats, and hung the hall with golden cloths and pictures. And when all was ready another great feast was held there, and the King gave Beowulf a banner, a helmet, and a coat of mail, all wrought with gold. His own rich and mighty sword he gave also to the hero. And to these gifts he added eight horses with cheek plates of gold, and on one of them was the gay silver saddle that was the King's own war saddle. And the Queen gave Beowulf golden rings and armlets, and a golden mantle, and the grandest collar in the world all set with jewels. All Beowulf's companions were likewise given precious gifts. And Heorot was filled with the sound of music.

After the feast the Goths and Danes lay down and slept once more in the hall; but Beowulf slept in a special room that had been made ready for him. If he had only slept in Heorot that night, it might have saved much sorrow.

For outside in the dark forest lived an old hag, Grendel's mother, at the bottom of a dreary pool. And when Grendel the Monster fled back to her and died, she was filled with rage. That night she came out of her pool and burst into the hall where the Danes and Goths were sleeping; and she fell on Beowulf's dearest friend, killed him, and fled away with his head.

In the morning when all was known, Beowulf cried to Hrothgar:

"Rouse up, guardian of the kingdom! Your men and mine must follow the track of the hag, and whether she hides in the dark forest, in the depths of the earth, or the bottom of the sea, she shall not escape me!"

So the Danes and Goths rode forth from Heorot, and followed Beowulf into the forest; and after a long time they found the dreary pool, and there on the brink of it lay the head of Beowulf's friend. Then the men blew a blast on their horns, and sat down by the pool. At the sound of the blast, strange creatures rose up in the water and swam about: sea snakes, water serpents and dragons. But they could not make the heart of Beowulf afraid. He put on his armor, bade the men watch for him, and plunged into the pool.

For nine hours the men sat and watched, but Beowulf did not return. Then the Danes would wait no more, but went back sadly to Heorot, to tell the King that Beowulf was dead. But the

Goths, who were Beowulf's own men, still waited by the pool.

Now when Beowulf leaped into the pool he began to sink, and the hag, who was waiting for him, seized him and bore him to the bottom. The pool was so deep that it took them the best part of the day. There Beowulf found himself in a strange hall, with a roof that kept off the water, and it was brightly lit with fire. The walls of the hall were hung with mighty weapons, and the floor was strewn with treasures. Further on lay the dead body of Grendel the Monster.

Now Beowulf and the hag began to fight, and Beowulf drew his great sword which had never failed him yet. But strange to tell the sword could not hurt the hag; when it touched her the edge of it turned aside. It was the first time Beowulf's sword had not served him. So he flung the sword away and grappled with the hag with his hands. First he flung her down, and then she rose up and flung him down; but her knife could not cut through his armor any more than his sword could cut through her skin.

Then Beowulf got on his feet again, and he saw amongst the weapons on the wall an old and monstrous cutlass, made for the use of giants. He snatched it from the wall and struck at the hag with it. Instantly she fell, and the fight was ended.

Now Beowulf made ready to return to the top of the pool; but first he picked up his own sword again. He would not take any of the treasure from the hall, the only thing he took was the head of Grendel as a sign that the monster was really dead.

When he came swimming up through the pool, his Goths rejoiced to see him whole and sound. They put the head of Grendel on a pole, and it took four of them to bear it through the forest. And so they marched once more to Heorot with Beowulf in their midst. When they entered Heorot, where the King and Queen sat among the Danes, all were startled at the sight of the head, but filled with joy because Beowulf was alive.

Then the King rose up and thanked and praised him, calling him his beloved Beowulf. And a new feast was made, and they drank till night grew dim above them, and it was time to sleep again.

But when the voice of the raven was heard at sunrise, Beowulf rose and said he must take ship again for his own country. And King Hrothgar clasped him, and kissed him, and wept; for the old King had come to love the young hero better than any other man.

So Beowulf, wearing his rich gifts of golden armor, went over the grass down to the sea where his swift ship lay at anchor. And he and the Goths got into the ship, and sailed away to their own land again.

BEOWULF THE GOTH

Grendel came to Heorot,
    The kingliest of halls,
And took his supper on the spot
    Within those golden walls;
On many a Dane he made again
    His meal with lips a-froth—
"But you shall not sup on me, Grendel!"
    Said Beowulf the Goth.

Grendel howled in Heorot
    Between the walls of gold,
For the strongest man alive had got
    The monster in his hold.
He caught him tight, as others might
    Have caught a little moth—
"And now your hour is come, Grendel!"
    Said Beowulf the Goth.

Grendel fled from Heorot
    With golden splinters strewn,
But the fair hall stood without a blot
    Before the next night's moon.
Now clear and strong rose sounds of song
    Instead of sounds of wrath—
"For you have supped your last, Grendel!"
    Said Beowulf the Goth.

The Quarrelsome Brother

ONE day King Bran of Britain sat on the rock of Harlech, and looked over the sea to Ireland. A bigger king than Bran was never born. There was no house big enough to hold him, so he lived in the open air, and slept under a tent.

On either side of King Bran stood his two brothers. One of them was fair and gentle, but the other was dark and quarrelsome.

At the feet of King Bran sat his sister Bronwen. No Princess ever had so white a skin as Bronwen, King Bran's sister.

Now as he sat on the rock King Bran said: "I see thirteen ships on the water."

And true enough thirteen ships came sailing from the South of Ireland. They had flags of satin on their masts and over the side of the foremost ship was a shield, with the point turned up as a sign of friendship.

When the ships reached the shore their chief stepped out and said:

"I am the King of Ireland. I come in peace to ask Bronwen for my wife. By our marriage Ireland and Britain will be joined, and both be stronger than they were before."

"We will talk about it," said King Bran. And he made the King of Ireland welcome, and had a banquet prepared under a tent. So they made merry together, and when the banquet was done Bran gave the King of Ireland Bronwen to be his wife.

And there, the two kings stayed for many days in the tents in the meadows, with their horses and people around them.

Bran's Quarrelsome Brother came into the meadows and looked at the horses of the King of Ireland, saying to himself:

"How dared they give my sister Bronwen to this man without asking me?" In his anger he drew his knife, and slashed at the King of Ireland's horses.

When the King of Ireland saw what had been done, he was full of sorrow and surprise. He thought King Bran, his friend, had done it, and he said:

"Bran could not have done anything to hurt me more than this."

The men of Ireland said: "Yes, Bran has insulted you! There is nothing to do but go back to the ships and sail away."

So the King of Ireland turned his back on the tents, and went away.

Now when Bran saw him going he sent a man to ask the reason, and the man came back with these words:

"The King of Ireland says his horses have been hurt, and he himself insulted in a way he cannot forget."

"Go back to the King of Ireland," said Bran, "and say it was not I who hurt his horses. If he will only come back and make peace I will give him a good horse for every one of his old ones. And I will also give him a silver staff as tall as himself, and a golden plate as broad as his face. And I will also give him a magic pot, which will bring a dead man to life if he is put in it."

When the King of Ireland heard this he came back to the tents and made peace. Once again the two kings feasted and were friendly in the meadows, and after some time the King of Ireland went away in his thirteen ships with his men, horses, silver staff, golden plate, magic pot and his beautiful wife Bronwen.

When they reached Ireland there was joy among the people there, and all the great ones in the land came to see their beautiful new Queen.

To each who came she gave a golden brooch, a ring, or some bright jewel. For a year she lived there happily, and presently a son was born to her and the King of Ireland.

But in the second year some of the chief men came to the King of Ireland and said:

"Though it is long ago, we cannot forget the insult that was done you when you were in Britain. You should never have made friends with Bran again or taken his gifts. As for Bronwen his sister, we will not have her for a queen any more. She shall be the cook in the kitchen, and every day the butcher who cuts up the meat shall give her a blow on the cheek."

So the beautiful Bronwen became their cook for three years, and did not know how to send word to King Bran of her misery.

Then one day she caught a young starling. She kept it in her kneading tin in the kitchen, and as it grew big she taught it to speak, and told it that her brother was King Bran of Britain. She wrote her brother a letter telling of her woes, and tied it under the starling's wing, and let the starling fly. Straight to King Bran in Britain the starling flew.

When King Bran read his sister's letter he was full of grief, and he said to his son Caradoc:

"Take charge of Britain while I am away, for I am going to Ireland to save my sister. And with me I will take the men of a hundred and fifty nations."

So Bran went to Ireland, and the ships of the nations covered the sea. But Bran himself walked in the sea, for no ship was big enough to hold him.

It happened that the swineherds of the King of Ireland were on the green shore with their pigs. When they saw the sea full of ships, and Bran walking beside them, they ran to the King and said:

"Sir, there is a forest of trees coming over the sea, and a mountain is coming with them."

For they thought the masts of the ships were trees, and King Bran himself a mountain.

But the King of Ireland knew who it was, and he called his chief men together in haste, and asked

But Bran himself walked in the sea.

what he had better do.

"Sir," they said, "the best thing to do is to go away over the river and break down the bridge so that King Bran and his men cannot follow. For at the bottom of the river there is a stone over which no ship can go."

Then all the people in Ireland went over the river and broke down the bridge.

When Bran came to the river his people said, "See King Bran, no ship can sail on this river, and there is no bridge over it. What do you say?"

"I say this," said Bran, "that the man who is a chief must also be a bridge." And he laid himself down across the river, and all his men passed over him from one bank to the other.

When the King of Ireland heard that Bran had crossed the river, he was full of fear. Once more he asked his chief men what he had better do.

"Sir," they said, "send a message to King Bran that if he will make peace you will give him your kingdom to do with as he likes. Say also that you will build him a house big enough to hold him, and that will please him, for he has never yet had a house of his own."

King Bran sent back word that he would make

peace when the house was ready.

Now the house had a hundred pillars to hold up the room. When it was ready the Irish chiefs stood two great leather bags beside every pillar. In each bag was an armed man, who was to leap out and kill King Bran when he came. But before King Bran came in, his Quarrelsome Brother slipped into the hall to try to find fault with it. When he saw the bags he laid his hand on one of them and asked:

"What is in this?"

"Meal, good soul," said the Irish chiefs. Then the Quarrelsome Brother squeezed the bag till the man in it was dead. And he laid his hand on the next bag, asking:

"What is in this?"

"Meal, good soul!"

The Quarrelsome Brother squeezed that bag too, and so he did with all the others.

Then Bran came safe into the house, and when he saw his sister Bronwen and the King of Ireland, there was peace once more between them. And Bran said:

"You have given me your kingdom to do with as I like. Now I in my turn will give it to your son and Bronwen's. So let the boy be brought in."

They brought in the King of Ireland's son, and all that saw him loved him—all but the Quarrelsome Brother, who did not want peace. The boy went from one to another, and every one embraced him.

Then the Quarrelsome Brother asked: "Shall he not come to me too?"

"Surely he shall," said King Bran.

But as soon as the boy came near, the Quarrelsome Brother laid hold of him, and killed him. At once every one sprang up and began to fight, and many were killed. But all through the fight Bran carried Bronwen on his shoulder under his shield, so that she should not be hurt.

The Irish chiefs then ran for the magic pot, and into it they began to throw their dead, so that they came out alive again. When the Quarrelsome Brother saw this, he lay down on the ground with the dead Irishmen, and was thrown into the pot with the others. And when he found himself inside it, he stretched himself out with all his strength, so that the pot broke in four pieces. But the Quarrelsome Brother broke his own heart at the same time. And the fight went on.

Out of that great fight between the King of Ireland and the King of Britain, they say that in all Ireland only five people remained alive. But who can say how much of this tale is true? Not I.

BRONWEN TO HER MAGPIE

My pretty bird with plumage black
    And strokes of white upon your wing,
Go fly, and make your airy track
    To Britain and to Bran the King.

Tell him beneath your wing to look,
    Where lies my letter all unseen;
Tell him his sister's now a cook.
    Who went from him as Ireland's Queen.

Tell him her sorrow is as dark
    As any feather in your tail;
Tell him she bears the stripes that mark
    Your wing upon her cheek so pale.

Tell him that Britain's Princess, who
    Once gay in Harlech danced and ran,
Weeps day and night for bitter rue;
    And tell him Bronwen waits for Bran.

The Little Island

I

THE Emperors of Rome had many lands.
Therefore, they wanted more lands still.

Over the sea lay the Little Island of Britain. "We'll
have that Little Island too," said the Emperors of
Rome, "and we'll build our towns in it."

But the Little Island did not want to belong to
the Emperors of Rome. She had kings and queens
of her own, for in those days, long ago, Britain
was a land of many kingdoms. In the West lived
Caradoc, the King of the Silurians in Wales. He
was the son of King Bran. And in the East lived
Prasutagus, the King of the Icenians, in Norfolk.
He had a brave queen for his wife, called Boadicea.

And then, too, the Little Island did not want to
have towns built on her, for in those days, long

ago, her people were rough and strong and lived in the wild country without towns. The marshes, the hills and the forests were their cities, and they had no roads, for they did not know how to make them.

Still, the Emperors of Rome kept their eye on the Little Island, and longed to have it. And one of them who wanted it was the silly Emperor Caligula.

"I am not a man!" said the silly Emperor Caligula to his people; "I am a god!" And he made the people bow down and worship him.

Then he had his favorite horse brought out of its stable and he laid his hand on its neck.

"This is not a horse," said the silly Emperor Caligula; "it is a priest!"

And he told his people he was going to make his horse the Chief Judge in Rome.

Then someone spoke of the Little Island of Britain, which even the great Julius Cæsar had not had time to conquer.

"Pooh!" said the silly Emperor Caligula, "*I* can conquer it!"

And he marched a great army out of Rome through Gaul to the sea, and there he got into a boat to go to Britain. But when he was halfway over—

"That's enough!" said the silly Emperor Caligula. "Go back again!" And the boat went back to Gaul. Then he said to his soldiers, "Fill your helmets with sea shells!" And his soldiers knelt down on the sands and filled their helmets with shells.

"And now we'll go back to Rome," said the silly Emperor Caligula. And the soldiers marched back to Rome.

When he got to Rome, the silly Emperor told the people that he had fought a battle with the sea, and conquered it; and that then the sea had paid him thousands of shells to go away and leave it in peace. "For I am the Conqueror of the Sea!" said he.

But the silly Emperor Caligula had never even seen the Little Island of Britain when he died.

II

Then came the Emperor Claudius, and he was another man altogether.

He too wanted the Little Island. But he really did cross the sea with his Roman soldiers, and he fought himself in Britain, and bit by bit conquered the land in the south. The wild Britons were driven farther back, fighting to keep the country for themselves.

None fought the Romans so long and so hard as the Welsh King Caradoc. He was brave and noble, but the Emperor Claudius was too strong for him. For nine years they fought together, and at last the army of Romans scattered his tribe of Britons far and wide. They took as prisoners Caradoc's wife and daughters, they made Caradoc's brothers give themselves up, and then they hunted Caradoc himself through the land.

Caradoc fled from his own kingdom of Siluria into the kingdom of the Brigantes. And coming before the Queen he said to her:

"See, you are a Queen and I am a King in Britain, but the Romans have killed my people and taken my family, and so I come to you for shelter."

But the Queen of the Brigantes was afraid, for she knew that the Romans would take her too if she tried to fight them. So instead of sheltering King Caradoc, she had him bound by her men, and taken to the Emperor Claudius.

The Emperor Claudius went back to Rome with Caradoc and his family as prisoners; and Caradoc said to himself, "He will put us all to death." And the Emperor marched through Rome, showing his prisoners to all the people, so that they might see what sort of strange kings there were in the Little Island.

Through the great streets of Rome walked Caradoc and his children, dressed in their rough clothes made of skins. But while the Romans looked at Caradoc full of curiosity, Caradoc looked at Rome itself full of wonder. For he had lived all his life in a wild country, and had never dreamed of a city with great temples, and tall columns, and fine roads, and mighty walls. So that as he gazed he could not help crying aloud:

"Oh, Emperor Claudius! you who already have such a splendid city and so much wealth and power, how could you wish to come to Britain to take my poor huts away from me and my family?"

Then the heart of the Emperor Claudius was touched, and instead of putting Caradoc to death he set him and his family free.

Some say they lived in Italy for the rest of their lives. But others say they went back to Britain,

Through the great streets of Rome walked Caradoc and his children.

where Caradoc ruled a part of the land again, as a subject of the Emperor Claudius.

III

The Emperor Claudius died, and then came the Emperor Nero.

The Emperor Caligula had been silly, and the Emperor Claudius kind; but the Emperor Nero was cruel. His cruelty was felt not only in Rome, but even in the Little Island far away, where now the Romans had a great part of the land, and were trying to get the whole.

Therefore when Prasutagus, the King of the Icenians, lay dying, he called to him his brave wife Boadicea, and said to her:

"When I die you will have no one to protect you from the Romans. So I have divided my wealth into two halves. One half I have left to you and our daughters, and the other half I have left to the Emperor Nero in Rome. For I hope this will soften his heart, so that he will treat you and my daughters and our people kindly."

Then Prasutagus died, and his wealth was

shared as he had said. But the half was not enough for the Emperor Nero. He wanted it all. And the Roman soldiers in Britain knew this, and they fell on the Icenians and plundered the country, and made slaves of the king's daughters, and had Boadicea whipped.

Then Boadicea, the brave Queen, was roused to anger, and she said:

"My Icenians have no King now to lead them, so I myself must act like a king, and lead them against the Romans."

She gathered together all her people into one great army, and led them to battle with a spear in her hand and a gold collar on her neck. Tall and strong was Queen Boadicea, but in the thick of the battle you could know her for a woman by her long, streaming hair.

At first she did much harm to the Romans, for just then the Roman General was away in the West of Britain. So Queen Boadicea led her people to the great cities which the Romans had begun to build in the Little Island: to Colchester, to Verulam, and to London. And she pulled down the cities and destroyed them, for she felt this was what would hurt the Romans most. They needed their cities to live in, but the Britons had always lived in the wild country, and hated the towns as though they were prisons. But soon the news reached the Roman General in Wales, and when he heard what had happened he came marching to London with his army.

There was no hope then for the brave Queen Boadicea. Although she had a bigger army than the Romans, she had no armor or weapons like theirs, and her soldiers were rough and untrained. Thousands of Icenians were killed that day in the battle near London, and only a few hundred Romans fell. Hour after hour Queen Boadicea fought with her spear, while her hair flowed down over her collar of gold. Hour after hour she saw her people fall around her.

At last she knew that the Romans had won, and she must soon become their prisoner.

"Rather than that," cried she, "I will die."

So saying, the brave Queen Boadicea fell on her spear and killed herself.

And thus the Romans, bit by bit, and battle by battle, became the conquerors of Britain, the Little Island.

THE EMPERORS OF ROME

There was a little Island
    Beyond the salty foam—
"We'll have that Little Island!"
    Said the Emperors of Rome.

So this one tried, and that one tried,
    And t'other one went home,
Till at last the Isle was taken
    By the Emperors of Rome.

But as a wet dog shakes itself,
    The island shook its loam,
Till it had shaken off its back
    The Emperors of Rome.

Attila, King of the Huns

IN THOSE DAYS, long ago, most of the world was a wild place. Here and there in some of the countries people had built towns and houses, and had emperors and kings to govern them. And when they were not at war these people lived quiet lives in their own homes, among their families.

But in the great wild lands that lay between the towns there were thousands of people who had no towns and no houses. They were as wild as the lands they lived in, and they wandered about the earth like herds of animals, spreading themselves over the countryside. By day they rode on their fierce horses, and at night they slept in tents. No one spot on earth was their home; but they ate and slept, now here, now there, thinking all the world was their own. Rough, savage men they were, hunters of wild beasts and drivers of cattle. They dressed in heavy skins and shaggy furs, and adorned themselves with beads and any bits of bright color they could get. These wandering tribes, whose horses' hoofs sounded like thunder as they rode, were the Huns, and the King of the Huns was Attila.

One day one of his shepherds saw a cow who had hurt her foot while she was grazing. The drops of blood lay on the grass where she had wandered. The shepherd followed the line of red drops on the green grass, till they led him to the point of an old sword that stuck up through the ground. He dug it up and brought it to King Attila.

"Ha, ha!" shouted Attila, "heaven itself has sent me the sword of Mars, the god of battles, to show that I by battle shall reign over the earth. And I shall be known to all men as the Scourge of God!"

In the middle of the plain he built a lofty altar made of fagots, and the Sword of Mars was stuck on high upon it. And once a year he made a sacrifice to the sword, of horses, and sheep, and every hundredth man he had taken prisoner in battle. This was the way of Attila, King of the Huns.

A large head, a dark skin, tiny eyes, big shoulders, a flat nose, a few hairs for a beard, a short, square body: that was the look of Attila, King of the Huns.

Wherever a town heard the thundering sound of his horses' hoofs scampering through the night, the people in their houses shuddered and shook, and whispered: "Here comes Attila, King of the Huns."

"No city shall ever catch me like a bird in a cage! But I will ride through all the cities of the world, and make the little kings obey me. For I am the greatest king of all! I am not the king of bricks and stones, but the king of the plains, and the forests, and the banks of the rivers!" So spoke Attila, King of the Huns.

Germany and Scythia, Persia and Illyria, Greece, France, and Armenia—through all these lands rode Attila, King of the Huns.

When the Emperor of Rome sent to make peace with him, he would not go into the city, not he!— he stayed in the middle of the plain, and he would not even get off his horse. "I'll do all my business on horseback. My horse is my house!" said Attila, King of the Huns.

And over the earth and over the earth he swept with his savage warriors, like a rushing river in flood. Five hundred miles at once, the mass of his armies covered, and cities fell before them by fire and sword. At last, in a lonely place on the banks of the Danube, where not a city was to be seen for thousands of miles, Attila built himself a palace.

Wooden sides and a wooden roof, all standing within a great wooden wall: and on the wooden wall were wooden towers and houses, and in each house lived one of his many wives— such was the palace of Attila, King of the Huns.

Inside this great palace made of tree trunks he heaped all the spoil he had taken from the cities: goblets of gold and plates of silver, saddles studded with gold and precious stones, shoes set with gems, rings, chains, and ornaments of every kind—these were the riches of Attila, King of the Huns.

His wives and warriors ate off gold and silver, and hung their necks and ears with jewels, and plaited their hair with bright colors; but Attila's own dress, his arms, and his horse's harness, were plain, without ornament, and all of one color. And he ate off wooden plates and drank out of wooden bowls, and ate no bread, but only meat. For he was too savage to care for what was fine or beautiful. So lived Attila, King of the Huns.

Once when in battle things went badly for him he made a pile of all the saddles on the horses' backs, and all their harness too. "And if I am in danger of being taken," said he to his men, "I will leap upon the pile and you shall set fire to it. For no man shall ever capture Attila, King of the Huns!"

But he was not taken, and did not burn on the pile. And still over the earth and over the earth he rode with his Huns, stripping the cities and trampling the ground. "Grass never grows where Attila's horse has trod!" cried he. And all the cities trembled. And at last Attila came to Italy, and threatened the greatest of all cities, Rome itself.

Then people began to wonder, "Will all the cities of the world be drowned by this terrible flood of Huns, or will something happen to save it?"

And something did happen.

For one night Attila, who already had a hundred wives, married one more, a beautiful girl called Ildico. To do this he went away from Italy for a while, and he made a great marriage feast for her in his wooden palace beyond the Danube. After hours of wild shouting and dancing and drinking, the Huns all slept on the floor. But when morning came they heard a strange sound in Attila's room, and when they went in there sat Ildico, weeping and wailing. But Attila lay dead on the bed.

Ildico said: "He burst a vein and died in the night." But had he died so, or had Ildico killed him? Nobody knows.

Then the Huns themselves began wailing for their savage King. They put his body in a coffin made of gold, and they put the gold coffin into a silver coffin, and the silver coffin into an iron one. Then they took it away to a secret place at night, and their slaves dug a deep grave, and laid the coffin in it. They covered it over with riches and jewels, and filled it in with earth. When all was done the Huns killed the slaves who had dug the grave, so that they never could tell.

And nobody knows to this day where lie the three coffins of Attila, King of the Huns.

THE RIDE OF THE HUNS

Attila rode with his Huns,
The rough and roving ones.
The folk in the cities crouched under
Their covers, and whispered, "Here comes
    the thunder!"

Attila rode with his Huns!
Under the blazing suns,
Under the night's black courses,
Sounded the gallop of Attila's horses.

Attila with his Huns
No longer rides and runs,
And only the stars that were peeping
Remember the place where King Attila's
    sleeping.

Duke Vortigern

CONSTANTINE, KING OF the World, was dead, and the lords of Britain quarreled as to who should be King of Britain in his place.

He had left three sons behind him, but Constans, the eldest, had given up the world and become a monk, and the two others, Aurelius and Uther Pendragon, were children, and not fit to rule the land. For the Picts had come out of Scotland in the north to fight the Britons, and they needed a man, not a child, to lead them. So the Barons argued and quarreled, but could not agree.

Now among the Barons was Duke Vortigern of Wales, who wished to be King of Britain himself. He had no right to the crown, and knew that he must get it by force or by cunning. So Vortigern went to Constans, the monk, and said:

"Your father the King is dead, and you were his

So Vortigern went to Constans the monk.

eldest son. Therefore, come back to the world, and be King of Britain."

"Alas!" said Constans. "I have been a monk so long that I have forgotten how to be a king."

"Leave that to me," said Duke Vortigern. "Only the son of the king can be king, but if you will sit on your father's throne, I myself will do the hard work and rule the country for you."

This pleased the poor foolish Constans, and he went to the palace and was crowned King of Britain. And he turned to none but Duke Vortigern for advice about ruling the country and fighting the Picts.

So now Duke Vortigern was nearly king, but he could not be content until he sat on the throne himself. He tried to think how he could kill Constans without the Britons knowing it, for in that case they would certainly kill him too. So Duke Vortigern went again to King Constans and said:

"The Picts are making new plans to fight you, but we do not know where or when. Now if I were king I would invite a hundred of the Picts to Court, and bribe them with money to spy on their brothers and tell us their secrets."

Poor foolish Constans had no mind of his own, and he sent at once for a hundred Picts to come and be his servants. And they came for the sake of money, and lived in the Court of Briton, but in their hearts they were still the enemies of King Constans.

Then Duke Vortigern went secretly among them, and praised and flattered them, and filled their pockets with gold, and gave them great skins of wine and strong drink, until their heads were turned. And the Picts said among themselves:

"King Constans is a poor sort of fellow, and our enemy. But this Duke Vortigern, who gives us drink is another sort entirely."

And full of drink they strolled up and down the streets singing:

"Duke Vortigern is worthy to be king! Duke Vortigern is worthy to be king!"

Then Vortigern came to them again in secret, and pretended to weep, saying:

"Alas, good fellows! I fear I must send half of you away. For the King keeps the money and does not give me enough to pay more than fifty of you for your service. Ah, if I were king you should all be rich!"

When Vortigern left them the Picts said among themselves:

"Why should we not be rich, and Duke Vortigern king?"

So saying, they rushed into the sleeping chamber of King Constans, and cut off his head, and carried it in triumph to Duke Vortigern. When Vortigern saw it his heart leapt for joy, but he did not show his joy. Instead he burst into tears, sprang up as though in anger, and called all the people of London about him. Then pointing to the Picts he said:

"See, these traitors from the north have killed our king! Let their heads too be cut off!"

So the hundred Picts were beheaded, and some of the Britons shouted that Vortigern must now be king, for he was used to ruling them. But others of the Britons thought that Vortigern was himself a traitor, though they could not prove it; and they took the two boys, Aurelius and Uther Pendragon, and fled into Cornwall, fearing for their lives.

THE SONG OF THE HUNDRED PICTS

A hundred Picts of Scotland
    Began to drink and sing,
Vortigern, Duke Vortigern
    Is worthy to be king!

Constans is a foolish monk
    With head shaved in a ring—
Vortigern, Duke Vortigern
    Is worthy to be king!

Aurelius is a fledgling yet,
    Too young to take to wing—
Vortigern, Duke Vortigern
    Is worthy to be king!

Uther Pendragon is a babe
    And dragons sometimes sting—
Vortigern, Duke Vortigern
    Is worthy to be king!

Vortigern he hid his face
    And wept like anything,
Vortigern, Duke Vortigern
    Became the British King;
And the hundred Picts from Scotland
    He hanged upon a string.

The Kings of Kent

W HEN D UKE V ORTIGERN became the King of Britain his mind was uneasy. For during the next few years the Picts in the north gathered great armies to come and avenge the death of their hundred brothers. At the same time in the south Aurelius and Uther were growing to be young men, and their friends were building great ships to sail against Vortigern.

Now as Vortigern wondered where he could turn for help, news was brought him that three longboats had arrived on the coast of Kent, full of armed men, strange and tall of stature. So Vortigern went down to see who they might be. Among them were two brothers still taller than the rest, and to these he spoke.

"What men are you?" said Vortigern, "of what birth? and whence come you?"

The cleverer of the two brothers answered him. "My name is Hengist," said he, "and this is Horsa, my brother, and these are all the best young men of the Saxon land in Germany, which is our birthplace. Now when more men are born in our country than it can hold, it is our custom to call the strongest men together, and choose by lot which must depart to find new lands to live in. This time the lot fell upon all of us whom you see here, and so we have come to your kingdom."

"You come in a good hour," said Vortigern, "for I am threatened by my enemies the Picts, and if you will help me to conquer them I will make you rich in lands and money."

So Hengist and Horsa joined their Saxons with Vortigern's Britons, and fought the Picts, and drove them back to Scotland. Then Vortigern gave the Saxons all he had promised. But in his heart Hengist wanted more than this. He was a Prince in his own land, and he wanted the power of a Prince in the new land he was to live in. So being clever he came to Vortigern and said:

"We have conquered the Picts this time, but they are sure to come again. Let me send to my own land for a greater army of Saxons to live here and help you in your battles. And further, as I am a Prince where I come from, let me have a city of my own, in which I may be known as a Prince."

"Send for your men, by all means," said Vortigern, "but as to making you a Prince in Britain, you are a foreigner and a heathen, and I dare not do it. My own people would be angry."

Hengist said: "I have served you well, and will serve you better. Grant me, if not a city, at least a castle, in which I may be called Prince. Just a castle, King Vortigern! And I will build it within the space of a single strip of leather."

To this Vortigern agreed; for he thought a single strip of leather could not enclose much space, and the castle would be a very small castle.

Hengist sent his messengers into Germany to fetch more Saxons, and he secretly bade them bring back his daughter Rowena too. Then he had a great bull killed and skinned. And he cut the bull's hide so cunningly that the whole of it made a single strip of leather of great length, and with this long strip he measured out the ground and built his castle. So the Saxons got their first foothold as rulers in Britain.

Presently Hengist's messengers returned with

eighteen boats full of Saxon warriors. Vortigern gave a royal banquet to welcome them. When the time for drinking came a lovely girl entered the hall, bearing a golden cup of wine, which she offered to the King. Amazed by her beauty, Vortigern asked who she was.

"This is my daughter Rowena," said Hengist.

"She shall be my Queen," said Vortigern.

"Nay," said the cunning Hengist, "can I part with my daughter without a price?"

"Name what price you will," said Vortigern.

Then Hengist spoke apart with his brother Horsa, and they decided that they would give Vortigern Rowena for his wife, if he would give them all Kent for a kingdom. And Vortigern, dazzled with Rowena's loveliness, agreed.

So Hengist and Horsa became the Kings of Kent. And year by year they sent for more and more of their people from Germany, until the Saxons in the east of Britain became as great a danger to Vortigern as the Picts in the north. For Hengist, wishing to be King of the whole land, turned on Vortigern, and fought him, till he fled for his life to his castle in the west. And there he was found and killed at last by Aurelius and

Uther, now grown to manhood. And these brothers in turn became King, and made peace with the Saxons, who settled in Britain then and for ever after; till in time they and the Britains seemed to be people of one race.

SAID HENGIST TO HORSA

Said Hengist to Horsa, "I see a white coast."
Said Horsa to Hengist, "I see a cocked oast."

Said Hengist to Horsa, "I think I smell hops." Said
Horsa to Hengist, "And sweet cherry-crops."

Said Hengist to Horsa, "We'll pitch there our tent.'"
Said Horsa to Hengist, "And be Kings of Kent!"

The Sword in the Stone

WHEN UTHER PENDRAGON came to die, England was left once more without a King. All the Lords of the land wondered among themselves who would be the next King.

Now there was living at that time a wise enchanter called Merlin. He could see into the future as well as into the past; and he had been the friend of Uther Pendragon, and knew his wishes. So Merlin sent messages to all the Lords, saying that they must come to London by Christmas to meet together in St. Paul's.

When the Lords came, there in St Paul's Churchyard they saw a great marble stone, and in the middle of it was stuck a sword. On the sword these words were written:

"WHOEVER PULLS THIS SWORD OUT OF THIS STONE IS THE TRUE KING OF ENGLAND."

One after another the Lords tried to pull out the sword, but though many of them were great Princes and strong Knights, not one could pull it out. They ordered ten Knights to guard the sword, and sent word through the country that on New Year's Day there would be a great tournament in London, which all the Knights and Barons in England must attend; and on that day perhaps the true King would be found among them.

On New Year's Day all the roads to London and all the London streets were filled with old Knights and young, riding to the tournament in their shining armor; and with them rode their ladies in their fine dresses; and their prancing horses had embroidered cloths of scarlet and blue and gold on their backs.

Among the Knights rode old Sir Ector and his son Sir Kay; and with them was Arthur, Sir Kay's young brother, a beautiful boy who was not yet old enough to be a knight.

Now on the way Sir Kay turned to Arthur and said: "Brother, what a fool I am! I have left my sword at home, and cannot fight in the tourney."

"I'll ride back and fetch it," said Arthur readily, and turned his horse's head, and galloped up the street. But when he got to Sir Ector's house it was locked, for all the people had gone to watch the tournament. So young Arthur could not get in to fetch Kay's sword.

When he had knocked in vain on the door, he grew impatient, and said to himself: "I'll ride to St Paul's Churchyard and take the sword out of the stone, for Kay must not be without a sword this day."

So off he rode again, and the Churchyard was as empty as Sir Ector's house, for the ten Knights had also gone to the tournament. With a quick, light tug, Arthur pulled out the sword, and rode away with it to his brother.

As soon as Kay set eyes on it he knew what sword it was. He showed it to his father, saying:

"Sir, here is the sword of the stone, so I must be King of the land."

Sir Ector was amazed, and when Kay had told all the story he called young Arthur, and the three returned to the Churchyard. There Sir Ector put the sword back into the stone and said:

"Now let us see! For only the true King of the land can pull it out."

So saying, he pulled himself at the sword, but it

did not move. Then Kay pulled, and still the sword stuck fast.

"Now let Arthur try," said Sir Ector.

"I will well," said Arthur, and pulled it out easily.

Then Sir Ector and Sir Kay knelt down before him.

"Alas!" said Arthur, "my own dear father and brother, why do you kneel to me?"

"My lord!"' said old Sir Ector, "it is time for you to know that I am not your father, and Kay is not your brother, except in love. Your true father was King Uther Pendragon himself, and the night you were born the enchanter Merlin carried you away from the castle, and gave you to me to bring up in safety."

Then Arthur was sad at heart, for he had always thought of good Sir Ector as his father, and he could not all at once feel glad of his real father, though it was King Uther Pendragon himself. Nevertheless it was the truth, and Arthur knew he must now be King in his turn.

On Twelfth Day the Knights and the Barons came to the Churchyard, and none of them could move the sword in the stone. But Arthur pulled it out before them all. Then they were angry that so young a boy should do what they could not do,

"The enchanter Merlin carried you away."

and prove himself their King; and they said:

"How do we know he is really the son of Uther Pendragon? Most likely it is a falsehood. Let us wait till Candlemas, and try again."

At Candlemas they came together and tried the sword again, and none but Arthur could move it. So the Barons said:

"Let us wait till Christmas!"

And at Christmas Arthur drew the sword again.

"Let us wait till Easter!" cried the Barons.

But at Easter none but Arthur could draw the sword, and the Barons shouted:

"Let us wait till Pentecost!"

Now Merlin the Enchanter searched through England, and got together all the Knights who had been loved and trusted by King Uther Pendragon. These men gathered round young Arthur, and swore to serve and honor him, and when Pentecost came they rode with him to the Churchyard. There were all the Knights and Barons waiting, and there too were all the common people watching. And once more Arthur pulled the sword out of the stone, with the whole of London looking on.

Then all the People shouted, and cried out:

"We will have Arthur for our King, for it is the will of God! Whoever is against it, we will kill him!"

And the great crowd, rich and poor together, knelt down to young King Arthur.

Arthur laid the sword upon the altar in the church and was crowned King. And he swore to be a true King to the Lords and the people all the days of his life.

The People, rich and poor, then spoke to him of their sufferings since the death of Uther Pendragon. Some had lost their land, and some their money; in some parts of the land roamed strange and dangerous beasts; in other parts lived giants, who killed the men and imprisoned the lovely ladies. And Arthur said:

"I will clear the land of all these evils."

Whenever he heard a new tale of wrong, he went himself, or sent one of his Knights on the adventure, to make all right again.

In his castle in Camelot he had a round table built, and here he sat with all the best Knights in England around him. And the greatest honor any man could have in those days was to be one of Arthur's Knights of the Round Table.

But if I tried to tell you all their names and their adventures;

If I began the tale of how King Arthur found a magic sword in the middle of a dark lake;

Or the tale of Guinevere, his lovely Queen;

Or the tale of Lancelot, his greatest Knight;

Or the tale of Merlin, his wise councilor, who was shut up in a tree, and perhaps is there to this day;

Or if I told you the tale of Arthur's death, and of the three fairy Queens who came in a black boat, and bore away his body to the Isle of Avalon in Somerset;

I would be old before I was done.

IS ARTHUR GONE TO AVALON?

Is Arthur gone
To Avalon
In a black boat, as I hear?
Yes, three tall Queens were there alone
To row and watch and steer.
Who saw him go
And told you so?
His Knight, Sir Bedivere,
Now Arthur's crown is fallen low,
His sword lies in the mere,
And Arthur's gone
To Avalon
With a black boat for his bier.

Ogier the Dane

THERE CAME A time, after King Arthur's death,
when in all the world there was no King so great
as Charlemagne, the Emperor of the Franks.

Two hundred years before he was King,
Muhammed was born in Mecca in the East.
According to tradition, when Muhammed grew
up, the angel Gabriel appeared and delivered a
message from God. Muhammed set out to teach
this message to others. Muhammed's followers
became known as Muslims and their religion is
called Islam.

In the early years of Islam, its leaders moved
into lands that were once part of the Roman
Empire. For hundreds of years there were battles
between the Muslims and the Christians.

Then Charlemagne, the Emperor of the Franks,
was born, and when he grew up he fought the

Muslim armies with all his might, wherever he found them in the Western lands.

And as once all the best Knights had gathered round King Arthur in England, so now all the best young men alive gathered round the Emperor Charlemagne in France. The twelve best of all he called his Paladins. In time there was no Paladin so great as Charlemagne's own nephew Roland; and with him was always his dear friend Oliver. But at the time of this story these two were still young squires.

It happened one day that the Emperor Charlemagne struck his forehead, and said:

"I remember something I have long forgotten. King Geoffrey of Denmark has fought the Muslims like me, and now his Denmark is a Christian land like my France. But France is a greater land than Denmark, and an Emperor is a greater man than a King. Therefore King Geoffrey must bow down to me."

So Charlemagne sent his messengers into Denmark to tell King Geoffrey this. But what did King Geoffrey answer?

"I won't bow down to Charlemagne," said King Geoffrey the Dane.

"Then," said the messengers, "the Emperor will send an army to take away your son until you do."

And sure enough Charlemagne sent a great army to Denmark and they took away Ogier, King Geoffrey's son, to keep till King Geoffrey bowed down.

Ogier was only sixteen years old. When he was born six beautiful ladies appeared round his cradle and gave him gifts, such as beauty, and courage, and strength, and the power to make people love him. Then they went away. Some said they were fairies. Whether they were or not, Ogier grew up to be as strong as a giant, as brave as a lion, as beautiful as the sun, as charming as a spring day, and as loving of heart as your own mother.

When he was brought into France before Charlemagne, all the Court Ladies and all the Paladins marveled at this wonderful young man who was their prisoner: Ogier the Dane.

Charlemagne meant Ogier no harm, he meant only to keep him until King Geoffrey bowed down. So Duke Namo took care of Ogier, and taught him all that a Paladin should know, and loved him like his own son. Half of the time Ogier was eager for the day when he should be a real

Paladin too; and the other half of the time he was sad, because his father would not bow down and set him free.

Then one day men came riding hurriedly from Italy into France, and threw themselves before Charlemagne, crying:

"O Emperor, save us! The Muslims have landed with a great army near Rome, and they mean to take the city with sword and fire!"

So the Emperor gathered his army and went to Rome with all his Paladins; and all the young squires went too, who were not yet Paladins, but hoped to be one day. Among them were young Roland, and his friend Oliver, and Ogier the Dane, and many more besides.

When they reached Rome, the Muslims were already in the city. Charlemagne advanced to attack them. The first ranks of his army were commanded by Duke Namo, and with him rode Ogier the Dane as his squire; but because he was too young to be a Knight, Ogier was not allowed to wear armor or carry a sword.

Now the greatest honor any man could have in battle was to carry Charlemagne's golden flag, the Oriflamme, and in this battle the Oriflamme was given to a knight called Alory. But Alory was a coward, though nobody knew it.

Duke Namo and Alory rode forward, and the fight began. But Ogier had to stay behind, because of his youth. Yet his courage and strength burned like fire in him, and he longed to go with the rest. And with him stayed the other youths who were still squires; Roland and Oliver too.

Suddenly Ogier saw Alory drop the Oriflamme, and turn his horse's head to flee away. When Ogier beheld the glorious golden flag lying in the dust he could bear no more. He snatched up a wooden club, and rushed into the fight; and all the other young squires rushed after him. With one great blow Ogier knocked Alory off his horse; he took Alory's armor from him and put it on himself, and hid his face in Alory's own helmet. Then he snatched up the golden Oriflamme and leapt on Alory's horse. He rode like fire through the Muslims, broke their front ranks, and scattered them right and left. Above the battle the bright flag fluttered like a flame. And behind him rode the happy young squires, who had all done as he did, and taken horses and armor from the dead men on the field.

The Oriflamme was given to a knight called Alory.

Now from behind came up the chief army of Muslims, and at the same moment came Charlemagne's chief army, led by the Emperor waving his magic sword Joyeuse. He met the Muslim chief and overthrew him; then two Muslims fell on Charlemagne, killed his horse, and threw him down. The Emperor thought that his last hour had come.

But Ogier saw him fall, and knew him by the eagle on his helmet. Still holding high the Oriflamme, he rode against the two Muslims. One he stunned with Alory's sword, and the other he pushed down with Alory's horse. Then with his strong young arms he lifted up the Emperor, and set him on the second Muslim's horse. Charlemagne looked at the golden flag he bore, and cried:

"Thanks, my brave Alory! I owe my life to you."

But Ogier was silent, and turned away into the thickest of the fray. He fought with all the young squires behind him, until the Muslims fled out of the city back to their own camp.

Then Turpin the Archbishop, who had fought like the rest, laid down his helmet and sword and took up his miter and crozier, and sang in praise of God for the day's victory.

And as he sang, over the battlefield came Ogier the Dane, covered with dust, but still bearing the Oriflamme; and behind him walked the little band of squires in armor. But as they were still young boys the armor was much too big, and clanked and rattled on them as they walked. So that Charlemagne was puzzled, and said:

"How is it that all my knights have shrunk, and become so little during the battle?"

But when Ogier knelt before him with the flag, the Emperor embraced him, saying:

"Thanks, my brave Alory!"

And Turpin the Archbishop raised his hand, and said:

"A blessing upon Alory!"

And still Ogier said nothing.

But it was more than the brave young Roland could bear.

"It is not Alory!" he cried. Running forward, he raised his friend's helmet, and all men saw that he who bore the Oriflamme was Ogier the Dane.

Then the other young squires pulled off their helmets too, and showed their flushed and merry faces.

Charlemagne and his Paladins burst out laughing, but they were filled with tenderness and admiration of these young boys pretending to be big Knights. And all the boys' fathers came forward and embraced them, but the Emperor himself embraced Ogier the Dane.

"Dear Ogier," he said, "today you saved my life, and from today you and your friends are Knights and my Paladins!" And he drew forth Joyeuse, his famous sword, and touched Ogier's shoulder with it, and afterwards the shoulders of all the other squires.

Then Roland and Oliver fell on Ogier's neck, and from that hour those three were brothers in arms.

In time King Geoffrey did bow down to Charlemagne, but Ogier the Dane remained in the Emperor's Court as one of his best Paladins.

He grew to be seven feet tall. It took two bushels of flour to make him an ordinary loaf, the quarter of a sheep was but a slice of meat to him, and he could drink ten pints of wine at a single draught.

THE GAY YOUNG SQUIRES

When Charlemagne went to war
    He left his squires behind him,
And all the squires were sore
    Because they had to mind him.
"Although we are not Knights,
    Yet we have Knights for sires,
And our hearts are big for fights!"
    Cried out the gay young squires.

When Charlemagne went to war
    And fell down in the battle,
The squires sprang to the fore—
    Oh, how their arms did rattle!
"Our bodies may be small,
    But great are our desires—
At least our hearts are tall!"
    Laughed out the gay young squires.

How Alfred Made the Peace

IN THOSE DAYS, long ago, the Danes came out of Denmark in their ships.

They were great rough men, with red and golden beards, blue eyes, and skins made ruddy by the salt wind and brown by the sun on the sea.

They were great pirates, too. They crossed the sea to other lands, and up and down the coasts they sailed, chasing other people's ships and taking from them all they had. Often the robber Danes came ashore for a short while, and fought the people living near the coast, and took their goods and cattle. Then off they sailed again, shouting and laughing and quarreling, with their ships full of the things they had taken.

And sometimes they stayed a long while on the land, and would not go away until the King of the country had paid them large sums of gold. So they grew rich and powerful, and were much feared by the home-staying people.

But presently these robbers grew tired of their restless life on the sea, and a feeling swept through them all that they would like to have their own homes on land of their own. They had long been used to taking other people's things, and now they thought they would take their land as well. So one great Danish pirate sailed to Iceland with many men, and settled there; and another Danish pirate, called Rollo, went with his men to the North of France, and settled there in Normandy, and a third Danish pirate, called Guthrum, brought all his men to the East of England. And from the east coast they spread themselves south and north and west, until the country was overrun with them as an old barn is with rats.

The Saxons to whom England belonged fled back before the Danes, further and further west and south, till only the kingdom of Wessex was left to them.

"We'll have that bit too," said Guthrum the Dane, "and then all this island of England will be ours. For I hear that the Saxon King is dead, and Alfred his brother is but a boy of twenty-three. What can a youth like him do against men like us?"

Guthrum's men shouted that this young Alfred should never be crowned King of England. They would make a great attack on him, kill him, take Wessex, and crown Guthrum King of the land.

But Alfred the Saxon was wise as well as young, and he loved England as no Saxon had yet ever loved it. In those days the Kings thought more of war than peace, but Alfred was different. He knew that nothing can grow in a garden where men are always digging up the ground and cutting down the plants. A garden, when it is prepared, wants to be left quiet in order to grow its fruit and flowers. And to Alfred, England was a garden which wars and quarrels were always stirring up and cutting down. He longed to see his land at peace, and the Saxons living free and happy lives on their own earth. He longed to put an end to the wild robberies of Guthrum and to make Christians of the Danes who wished to kill him. He longed for England to have a time of quiet, so that the lives of her people might grow full and beautiful like flowers, and fruitful like trees in an orchard.

But, alas! before this could be, there must be more battles. For not till he was crowned King of England could he begin to plant his thoughts and plans for England's good, like seeds in the garden.

So Alfred gathered about him all his friends and followers in the kingdom of Wessex, and when the

Danes began their great attack he was ready for them. Eight battles in one year he fought, and at last drove the Danes back from the Wessex border. Then and only then he mounted the throne and was crowned King.

But Alfred knew the Danes would come again. He knew that peace could not yet be, and until there was peace he could do nothing for his dear England. He set his friends to watch at all the points along the Wessex border where the Danes might try to break through. But he had not enough men to guard it all, and Guthrum the Dane was cunning.

"This young Alfred," said he, "is chiefly guarding the river Thames. So we will not enter Wessex by the Thames, we will go west to Wareham, and fall on him when he doesn't expect us."

True enough, Wareham was a weak spot, and there the Danes broke into Wessex. More battles were won and lost, and then for the second time Alfred drove the Danes out. But still he had no hope of peace for England.

Guthrum the Dane swore: "The third time I will break this young Alfred, or be broken myself." And he gathered his men for the third attack.

This time fortune was with Guthrum, and against Alfred. The Saxons fled in confusion before the

All she saw was a ragged, dirty man.

Danes. Many ran to the coast, got their ships, and sailed away; many were killed, and many hid themselves in the tangled woods, or escaped into the Somersetshire marshes. Alfred no more could look upon his band of friends and followers. They had all vanished, and he was alone, a King without subjects, a ruler without a country.

He too had to flee before the furious Danes, he too had to hide in the woods and wander hungry in the watery marshes. One day in his wanderings he came to a neatherd's hut in the wood, and entered it. The neatherd's wife was stooping over the hearth, turning her cakes.

"Who's there?" she cried, fearing some dangerous enemy. But all she saw was a ragged, dirty man, with gentle, troubled eyes. She did not know that he was Alfred the King.

"I'm tired, goodwife," said the ragged man. "Can I sit down?"

"Yes, you can, I suppose," she grumbled. "But I must go see to the goats. Make yourself useful as you sit there, and watch my cakes and don't let them burn."

Then she left him, and Alfred sat down. But he stared at the fire, and not at the cakes. He stared at the fire and dreamed of his dear England, for which he could now do nothing. And he thought:

"My friends are all scattered, but they are somewhere. If I can find them, one here, one there, until we are a little band again, who knows but I may yet do something to make England like a lovely garden?"

Crack! came a great blow on his ear. The woman had returned, and her cakes were as black as cinders. The King had let them burn while he was dreaming.

Crack! came another blow. "Take that," the angry woman cried, "for spoiling my good cakes, you good for nothing!"

But Alfred was still good for something. He made his fireside dream come true. One here, one there, he found his friends in hiding, and on the Isle of Athelney in Somerset he built a secret fortress where they hid themselves. And day by day they slipped out into the countryside and wherever they found people they whispered Alfred's name; so soon, in all parts of the West Country, little groups gathered together, ready to follow Alfred when the time was ripe.

During this time of waiting and gathering, Alfred put on the humble dress of a minstrel, and with a harp on his back went to the camp of Guthrum. Minstrels were welcome men in those days wherever they went; for men had no books or printed music, and all their tales and songs were those they heard from the lips of wandering singers and story-tellers. So the Danes let Alfred sit among them, not knowing who he was; and when he had sung for them, they talked freely of their plans. And Alfred listened, and made his own plans all the better for knowing theirs.

He went back to his friends in Athelney, and said the time was ripe. The secret word went out to his people, and they all came together to meet him at a trysting place. When they saw Alfred the

King again, their hearts rejoiced. Two days later, full of hope, they marched to Ethandun, and fought and conquered the Danes.

Once more the Danes were driven out of Wessex, but this time Alfred followed them to their fortress and besieged it for fourteen days. Then Guthrum sent word:

"I give in. You have won. What are your terms?"

And Alfred answered: "Peace for England." And so King Alfred and King Guthrum signed the peace which was called the Peace of Wedmore— "For themselves and for their children, both the born and the unborn." And the Danes were to dwell upon one side of the rivers Thames and Lea and Ouse, and the Saxons on the other. And Guthrum agreed to worship no more the old gods of Denmark, but to become a Christian.

So Guthrum was christened, and changed his name to Athelstan; and Alfred stood godfather to him, and at his manor in Wedmore made a great festival for Saxons and Danes alike.

After eight days, Guthrum departed to the east side of the three rivers, and Alfred stayed on the west side.

Then at last he began to make wise laws for his dear England to which he had given peace.

THE KING'S CAKE

King Alfred he could sing a song
  As sweet as any man's;
King Alfred he could fight a throng,
  And think out battle plans;
King Alfred from his heart so true
  The English Laws could make;
But one thing Alfred couldn't do—
  He couldn't bake a cake.

I'd rather be like Alfred than
  Like any other King;
I'd rather, more than any man,
  Hear Alfred play and sing;
I'd rather keep, for England's sake,
  The laws he made for me—
But I'd rather eat my Mother's cake
  Than Alfred's for my tea.

The Treasure of the Isle

A LONG TIME ago there was a little boy called Olaf, who lived like a slave in Russia. And yet he was a King's son.

But his father was killed in Norway before Olaf could remember, and his mother fled away, or she and her baby would have been killed too. For a long time she hid in the reeds and forests, and wandered through the snow of that cold North Country, until she came to Russia. There she was captured by strange people and sold as a slave; and Olaf, a tiny boy, was sold too, but to another master. So the mother and son were parted, and lost to each other.

But Olaf knew he was a King's son, and he grew up a strong and jolly boy, always eager to be doing things, and sure he would not be a slave all his life. One day he met a man in Russia who was a powerful Lord in that country. This man looked keenly at Olaf and said:

"You are not a Russian boy."

"No," said young Olaf, "my father was a King of Norway, and I am Olaf his son."

"I was kinsman to the King," said the Lord, "and you shall be a slave no more, but shall live in my house like a Prince."

Olaf went to live in his kinsman's house, but as he grew older he became impatient to be doing something. One day he meant to win back Norway for his own, but he said to himself:

"It is easier to get a ship than a country, and before I am King of the land I'll be King of the sea."

So he got a ship, and men to follow him. This was easy, for he had a way that made men love him. And now, the King of his ship, sailed the sea between the coasts of Norway and England, fighting the other ships he met, and often landing on the English shore, getting money from the people like the pirate that he was. In those days the chiefs in the northern countries were nearly all pirates, and called themselves Sea Kings, and thought nothing of robbing ships and towns wherever they went. And Olaf, though he had as yet no country of his own, became the strongest and richest Sea King of them all, the most feared by his enemies and the most loved by his friends. He cared nothing for danger, and would go to meet it laughing.

Now one day he began a long voyage all round England, and when he had sailed up north and down south he heard tell of a lonely little island still further south, on which lived a wonderful holy man who was a Christian. Young Olaf was not a Christian himself. Like all the people of Norway in those days he prayed to the old heathen gods, and especially to Thor, the god of thunder and battles. But the tale of the holy man of the isle made Olaf curious, and he went in search of him.

At last he found him living in a cave on a little island surrounded by a sea as blue as sapphires. In the cave there was a cross, the sign of Christ. And the island was golden with daffodils, and so full of sweet flowers that Olaf could smell their scent on the sea even before he came ashore.

As he stepped out of his boat the old man came to meet him, and said gently: "I know you. You are Olaf, the pirate Sea King."

"Yes," said Olaf, "but I have not come to steal

your gold."

"You are welcome to all the gold in the island," said the old man, pointing to the daffodils, "and to one other treasure too."

"What treasure is that?" asked Olaf.

"This Cross," said the old man.

Olaf stayed some time with the old man, and they talked long together of Christ and of Thor. And in the end Olaf cried:

"I believe in Christ, and not in Thor any longer, and when I am King of Norway I will make my land a Christian land, and destroy the images of the heathen gods."

Then the old man baptized him, and Olaf sailed away.

ISLAND GOLD

When Olaf went a-pirating,
Long before he was a King,
He came ashore and made men pay
Him sums of gold to go away.

But when he came to Scilly's Isle
He stepped ashore and stayed awhile
Among the sunny fields and hills
That were all gold with daffodils.

And from the shore when Olaf went
He still could smell the island scent,
For he bore a gold flower in his coat
And a gold Cross upon his boat.

Queen Sigrid's Collar

IN TIME OLAF really did win Norway back, and became its King.

The people welcomed him and loved him, because he was strong and beautiful, did bold deeds, spoke good words and had a merry laugh. They were not always pleased when he began to go through the country pulling down the old temples of Thor, and telling the tale of Christ. But more and more as they listened to him they agreed to become Christians, and let him baptize them. In two years nearly all the people in Norway were Christians, and King Olaf's name was the greatest in the Northern world.

But in the kingdom of Sweden, which lay alongside of Norway, the people were still heathens. Over them ruled Queen Sigrid the Proud. She was said to be the most beautiful and the most dangerous of living Queens. Many Kings came wooing her, but either she sent them away, or set fire at night to the houses they were sleeping in. By morning her suitors could trouble her no more; they and their houses were a heap of ashes.

King Olaf of Norway knew this well enough, but he was never one to hold back from danger. "And," said he, "it is fitting that the strongest King and the proudest Queen in the world should wed one another."

So he sent his offer to Queen Sigrid by a messenger, who also bore to her as a present an immense collar of gold.

Olaf had found it on the neck of the image of Thor, when he was destroying one of the old temples.

When Sigrid saw the great gold collar, she was full of joy. She gave it to her goldsmiths and said:

"Out of this heavy gold you shall make a more beautiful collar for me to wear."

But the goldsmiths weighed the collar in their hands, and said nothing.

"What is the matter?" asked Sigrid the Proud.

"O Queen!" they said, "we fear that this collar is not real gold."

Then she commanded them to break open the collar; and true enough it proved to be only a copper collar after all, with just a thin covering of gold on top.

Queen Sigrid the Proud started up in a rage, and swore that Olaf had insulted her. Soon after he came to see her, and at the sight of him she almost forgave him for sending her a copper collar instead of a gold one. And she had nearly agreed to marry him, when King Olaf said:

"The wife I marry must give up the worship of Thor, and become a Christian."

"That I will never do!" replied Queen Sigrid.

"Then," said Olaf, "you are not the wife for me." And flicking her a tiny blow with his glove, he went away.

This time Sigrid the Proud sat quite still in her rage, and said: "That little blow, King Olaf, shall cost you dear."

The years went by, and Sigrid became wife to the King of Denmark, who had a beautiful young sister called Thyri. They wished to marry her to a certain old King whom she could not bear. For six days Thyri sat at the wedding-feast, and would not eat or drink. On the sixth night she slipped away and fled into Norway. She had never seen King Olaf, but she knew he was strong and beautiful, and she hoped he would be kinder to her than her own brother. So she went to his Court to beg him to protect her, and as soon as she saw him she loved him. And Olaf loved Thyri, and made her his Queen.

Now there was certain land that belonged to Thyri, because she was the Princess of Denmark. But when her brother the King of Denmark, and Queen Sigrid his wife, heard that she had married their enemy Olaf, they were full of anger. And they refused to give up the land.

So Olaf made ready his warships, and prepared to sail from Norway. He first meant to speak about Thyri's land, and then, if need be, to fight for it. He had the finest warships in the world, long narrow ships called Serpents; and best of them all was the Long Serpent, the ship he sailed in himself. In Sweden and Denmark they heard he was coming.

Then up spoke Queen Sigrid, who had never forgiven Olaf in her heart for the copper collar and the blow from his glove. She spoke in her hate to the Kings of Denmark and Sweden, and all the great Northern Kings who sailed the Baltic Seas.

"Here comes this Olaf," said Sigrid, "to threaten us all with his ships, as though he were the hero of the North! And he is only the King of little Norway after all. Will you let him have his way with us all?"

Then all the Kings bestirred themselves, and secretly prepared their ships; and they sent a great Earl into Norway to spy upon Olaf, and send them word of his coming.

This traitor Earl pretended to be Olaf's friend. "Let me sail with you," said he, "for my business takes me too where you are going." And Olaf suspected nothing and welcomed him.

But the traitor Earl delayed Olaf until he knew the other Kings were ready. Then on a summer day the Serpents sailed out among the islands of the Baltic Seas. The Earl's ship led the way, and last of all came Olaf in the Long Serpent. The shields of his men hung on the sides of the ship, and flashed in the sun. And hidden in a bay of the sea, behind a cape, lay all the ships of all the Kings of the North.

Straight to this bay the traitor Earl led Olaf's

Beside him kneeled the archer Einar.

shining fleet—one by one the Serpents came round the cape among their enemies. As each one came it looked so splendid that the Kings of the North said to each other:

"This must be the Long Serpent, with Olaf in it!"

But one who knew it always answered: "No this is not the Long Serpent yet!"

At last the Long Serpent itself flashed round the cape, and Olaf found all his ships facing all the fleets of the North Seas.

His captains said:

"There is bad work here. The Earl betrayed us. Let us go back."

But Olaf stood high on his quarter-deck, and cried: "I never yet fled from danger, and I never will! Strike the sails, and let God do as he will with our lives."

All day the battle raged, and Olaf shone above it all. He stood upon his quarter-deck in a short red coat, a gleaming helmet, and a golden shield, calling cheerily to his men, and throwing daggers with both hands at once, that never missed their aim. Beside him kneeled the archer Einar, the best archer in the world.

One by one Olaf beat back the fleets. But one by

one he lost his own ships, till at sunset the Long Serpent was left alone. And still his daggers and Einar's arrows kept the enemy at bay. Then one of them shot an arrow at Einar's bow, and broke it. Olaf heard the crack, and said:

"What has just broken, Einar?"

And Einar answered: "Norway, from your hand, King Olaf."

The enemy came near, and leaped on board, and Olaf fought until he had scarcely one man left. And he knew the end had come, but he would not be taken.

For the last time he stood up in his ship, and then in his red coat he sprang into the sea, red with the sunset. Deep under the waters he sank, and was seen no more.

But because no man had really seen him die, they often said in Norway: "Who knows? Perhaps King Olaf is not dead. Perhaps one day he will come again."

AND WILL KING OLAF COME AGAIN?

And will King Olaf come again,
Oh, will King Olaf come again?
We saw him leap into the main
And never saw him come again.

The northern sea was red with pain,
The sky had got a crimson stain,
When Olaf fought with Swede and Dane
As no man ever fought again.

Will King Olaf come again?
Will King Olaf come again?
Some say Olaf has been slain,
And some say he will come again.

The Church and the Crown

THERE WERE ONCE two cousins, King Edward of England and Duke William of Normandy.

It was a beautiful corner of France that Duke William ruled over—a country full of apple orchards, and flowery meadows, and tall poplar trees rustling on the banks of the River Seine. Duke William liked the work of ruling, and he ruled his corner of France wisely and well.

One day he took ship for England, to visit King Edward, his cousin. And as soon as he set eyes on England he loved it, and longed to have it for his own.

"Why not?" thought Duke William. "For King Edward has no son to come after him, and as we are cousins I'll ask him to leave his crown to me."

So William asked his cousin to let him be King of England when Edward was dead, and Edward, too, said pleasantly:

"Why not?"

During the visit they became good friends, for Edward loved the French people well, and William at last went back to Normandy laden with presents given him by Edward. And in his heart he was sure that he would one day be King of England.

But as to Edward, he never gave it another thought. All he really thought about was building a great church at Westminster, for he was a King who cared more for a church than for his crown. And when William had asked him for the crown of England, it was to Edward just friendly talk. He knew he had not really the power to say who should be the King of England when he himself was dead. All he could do, when he was dying, would be to tell the Wise Men of England whom he would like to be King. For when the King had no son the Wise Men of England chose the next King of the land. And they would never have dreamed of choosing Duke William of Normandy. He was a Frenchman, and the Wise Men thought that England ought to be ruled by an Englishman. So they looked round among the English nobles

He was a real Englishman.

for the man who was the bravest and strongest, and had done the best for his country.

Harold, Earl of Wessex was this man. He was a real Englishman, and the King's own brother-in-law; and he was wise and noble too. While King Edward still sat on the throne, all men knew in their hearts that nobody in England was so fit to rule them as Harold, or would one day make so good a King as he. But before King Edward died, Harold fell into great danger.

For one day as he was sailing the seas between England and France, his ship was wrecked, and he was thrown up on the French shore. And there he was found by Count Guy, the Lord of the Manor. Count Guy knew him at once; all men knew Harold, the great Earl of Wessex, whose sister was married to the King of England. So when Harold asked him for help and shelter—

"Ho, ho!" cried Count Guy, "do you not know that everything the sea washes up on this part of the shore is mine, because I am the Lord of the Manor? Sometimes it is great planks of wood from the wrecked ships, the ship's figure-head itself, a golden dragon, or a painted serpent's head, or perhaps an oar, or a jeweled cup, or a soldier's shield. But whatever it is, it is mine, for I am Lord of the Manor! And today, Earl Harold, the sea has washed me up a man—so you are mine too!"

And Count Guy called his men, and had Harold put in prison, saying he must stay there until some one in England paid a great sum of gold to set him free.

Harold was angry at such bad treatment, and he managed to send a message to Duke William of Normandy, who was Count Guy's master. Duke William came at once, and made Count Guy let Harold go; and he took Harold back with him to the Norman Court, and treated him as a friend.

But in his heart he was not quite Harold's friend, for he knew that when King Edward died all England would want Harold to be the King.

"Now is my chance," thought Duke William, "to settle it for good and all, while I have Harold in my power."

So instead of letting Harold go, he kept him with him for a long while, and Harold helped him fight his battles. He was so brave and strong that William's wife, the Duchess Matilda, and all her ladies, did a great picture in needle-work of the battle, and put in the figure of Harold taller than any other, holding up two Norman soldiers at once.

After the battle Duke William said to Harold: "You have fought so well for me that I will make you my Knight, after our Norman way."

So Harold kneeled before William and swore to be his man. And some say that William would not let Harold go until he had also sworn to let William be King of England when King Edward died. But whether Harold swore this or not, he had no power to say who should be King of England. That power lay only with the Wise Men.

Presently, however, Duke William let Harold return to England. And feeling sure at last of the English crown, he waited in his own beautiful country for the death of King Edward.

It came to pass near Christmas time that Edward fell ill, and knew that he must die. He still thought of his church and not of his crown; and he prayed God to let him live long enough to see the great church of Westminster finished before he closed his eyes. This happiness was granted him. At Christmas he called all the Wise Men to him in London, and the day after Christmas the church of Westminster was blessed, and made fit for worship.

"Now I can die happy," said the King, "for my church is ready."

"But what about your crown?" asked the Wise Men. "Whom would you like to wear it when you are dead?"

The King said: "Let Earl Harold have my crown." And soon afterwards he died, and was buried in his own church at Westminster.

Then early in the year the Wise Men let it be known that they would choose the new King of England. And they said:

"Our choice is Harold, Earl of Wessex, and he was also the choice of King Edward who is dead. And we choose him because he is the best man in England. Therefore, Harold shall be King of the English and Lord of the Isle of Britain."

And all the people of England rejoiced in their new King.

But over the water in Normandy Duke William heard the news and shook his fist. And he sent word into England:

"The crown of England is mine by right, for three reasons. The first is that I was King Edward's cousin. The second is that King Edward promised me the crown. And the third is that Harold swore to be my man and let me be King."

But the Wise Men answered:

"In the first place, cousins do not count; the King of England is made by choice alone. In the second place, King Edward had no power to promise you the crown. And in the third place, Harold cannot be your man against the will of the English people."

Then Duke William said to himself:

"There is a fourth reason for my being King of England, and it is that I want to be King of England."

He sent word through France that Harold had broken his oath and was a traitor; and he called upon his Normans and all his French friends to follow him to England to fight for the Crown.

NORMAN WILLIAM

Had I been Norman William
With orchards such as these,
With fields so green and flowery,
With such tall poplar trees,
And with the bright broad Seine
Curling through hill and plain,
The thought of Harold's England would
have tempted me in vain.

Had I been Norman William,
Possessing for my goods
Fairy-tale thatched cottages
And fairy-haunted woods,
I would have passed my days
Afar from battle frays,
Drinking sweet apple cider at the Inn of
the Four Ways.

The Fall of the Golden Man

When King Harold heard that Duke William was calling up the men of France to help him to fight for the English crown, Harold himself called up the men of England to help him to keep it.

Harold did not know when William was coming, but he knew it would be soon; and he did not know where his ships would land, but he knew it would be somewhere in the South. So when he had gathered his men, he set them to watch all along the South Coast for the first sign of William's ships.

But the days went by, and William did not come. And Harold's men waited and waited until at last there was nothing more to eat in that part of the country. Then the men would wait no more, and went back to their homes. And at last Harold himself had to go too, to a battle in the North of

England, where his own brother was fighting for the crown. And while Harold was winning that battle up in the North, with all his men behind him, Duke William came in his ship to the South, and there was no one to stop his landing.

Duke William sprang ashore on England, which he wished to make his own, and as he sprang he stumbled and fell, with his hands spread out to save himself. When he got up, each hand held a fistful of the earth he had grasped.

Now his men had looked uneasily at each other when they saw Duke William fall the moment he set foot on English soil. It seemed to them a bad sign. To all but one, who cried out heartily:

"That's a good sign, my Lord Duke! See, you have already taken hold of England in your hands."

For that saying, the Duke later on made him a rich man.

Then he and his men marched to Hastings, where they quickly built up a castle of wood. There they lived, and went forth day by day, to rob and fight the people of Sussex.

Soon the bad news was brought to King Harold, and his heart grew heavy within him.

"Ah," said he, "if only I had been there, Duke William would never have set foot on England. But I could not be in both North and South at once."

Once more Harold sent word through the land, calling his men together to march with him to Sussex and drive out Duke William and the Frenchmen. Six days he stayed in London, gathering his army, and meanwhile he sent a message to Duke William, to see whether the battle could not be avoided, and much pain spared. So King Harold offered him money to go away.

"What!" cried Duke William, "does he treat me as though I were a Danish pirate, landing in England without any right? I am here because England is *my* country, not his, and I would not leave it for all the gold in the world."

Then he in turn sent a message to Harold, saying:

"It is a pity for many men on both sides to die, when the quarrel is only between you and me. Let us two fight it out alone, and he who wins shall be King."

But Harold knew that such a fight would not end the matter, whoever won, and he sent answer:

"This is not my quarrel only, it is the quarrel of the people of England."

So after six days, when Harold had got together the men of London, of Wessex, of Sussex, and of Kent, he marched South to Hastings. There he pitched his camp beside an apple tree on the hill of Senlac, and waited for Duke William and his Normans to come.

Now the English were used to fighting with the Danes; for these old pirates, like themselves, fought on foot with shields and daggers and axes. Their way was to stand side by side, making a sort of long wall with their shields on their left arms, while they threw daggers at each other with their right hands. And then they rushed in upon each other with their axes.

But the Normans fought in a new and cleverer way. Many of the soldiers were good archers, and many of them rode on horses. Harold knew that if his own men tried to march afoot to meet the Normans in the open field, the Norman archers could easily shoot them down with arrows from a distance, and the Norman horsemen trample them down close at hand.

So he spoke to his men, and said:

"We must fight this battle in a new way. We must stay on the top of the hill, and make a wall of our shields, and let the Normans try to come up to us. Their horses will not find it easy to ride uphill, and as they come we will throw down our daggers at them, and as they get near we will strike them with our axes. But whatever we do, we must not rush out into the open field. We must stay together on the hilltop, and keep our shield wall firm."

On the morning of the battle Duke William rose early, and called for his coat of mail. But when he had put it on, one of his men said:

"My Lord Duke, you have turned your coat back to front!"

Then Duke William laughed, and said:

"That is another good sign, and shows that I this day will be turned from a Duke into a King."

And he would not change it, but rode into battle on his great horse, carrying an iron mace in his hand, and wearing his armor hind part before.

That same morning King Harold also rose early, and posted his troops all ready, so that they made a wall of shields all round the hilltop. He took up his own post between his two flags—one the

Royal Standard, worked with precious stones, and the picture of a Fighting-Man in gold; the other the Golden Dragon, the famous old flag of Wessex.

At last they saw the Normans coming up the hill, and in front of them all rode, not Duke William, not a soldier, but a minstrel singer juggling with his sword. Cut-Iron was this man's name, and he had begged Duke William to let him ride in front and strike the first blow. So up the hill to battle he rode, throwing his sword high in the air, and catching it as it came down. And all the time he was singing songs of Charlemagne, the great Emperor of France, and of Roland, his bravest Paladin. Up the hill to battle rode Cut-Iron, singing and juggling. And he killed the first man with his sword, and the second with his lance, and then Cut-Iron himself was cut down with his song on his lips.

And the Normans toiled up the hill after him, and the Englishmen thrust them back. Whatever the Normans might do, they could not break the wall of shields. In the fiercest of the fight stood King Harold, fighting beneath his two great flags. At last the Normans began to fall back and fly,

. . . Throwing his sword high in the air.

and the Englishmen wanted to follow them. Those who did follow were quickly killed, but Harold shouted:

"Stay where you are on the hill! Only keep the shield wall firm, and you cannot be beaten!"

And most of the Englishmen returned quickly to the hill.

The cry now went up that Duke William was killed, but this was false. When the Duke heard the cry he tore the helmet from his head so that all men could see his face, and he cried:

"I live, and by God's help I will conquer!"

And once more he led his men back to the battle, trying to make his horses break through the English shield wall. For he saw that until this was done the battle could not be won. But the English held their shields fast, and the wall stood firm.

So now Duke William thought of a cunning trick, to lure the Englishmen down from the hill. He sent orders secretly to his army to turn and fly as though they were beaten and could fight no more. When the English saw the whole French army in flight, they thought they had won the day, and they could no longer resist rushing down the hill after them.

In vain King Harold shouted to them to stay

where they were. It was too late. The shield wall was broken. And as soon as they saw this, the Frenchmen turned on the English in the open field, and trampled them under their horses, and shot them down with their arrows.

Now only Harold and his own special men remained on the hilltop. Together they stood there, making their own little shield wall against the Normans. The autumn twilight was falling as the Normans came once more upon them. There for a while Harold fought on bravely, while the Golden Man and the Golden Dragon fluttered over his head, and his shield was all stuck over with the Norman arrows. All who came near him were struck down by the mighty swing of his great battle-axe. But the archers stood at a distance and aimed always at the King. And at last a well aimed arrow pierced him through the eye, and King Harold fell.

Then in rushed the Normans to take the flags. And they bore off the Golden Dragon to Duke William in triumph. But the Golden Man fell beside the King, and was trampled underfoot.

And so Duke William of Normandy became King William of England.

THE HOAR APPLE TREE

Gold fell the autumn leaf
Over hill and lea
When Harold pitched his camp
By the hoar apple tree.

Gold fell the evening sky
Over land and sea
When Harold fought his last
By the hoar apple tree.

Gold was the Fighting-Man,
Royal gold was he,
That fell when Harold fell
By the hoar apple tree.

This index provides a list of the most important names in the book, a pronunciation guide for each name, and the page(s) on which the name is referenced.

Index with Pronunciation Guide
Pronunciation Key

This list of the most important names in the book tells you on what page you may find each name and how to sound those you may not know.

Sound	In These Words	Sound	In These Words
a	map, pat	o	pot, stop
ā	ate, face	ō	over, go
â	care, pair	ô	order, all
ä	far, farther		
		u	cut, butter
e	pet, west, head		
ē	we, meet	oi	boil, voice
		ou	shout, house
i	in, bit		
ī	nice, tiger	o͝o	pull, put
		o͞o	rule, move, use, music

ə represents:

a	in about	o	in lemon
e	in token	i	in happily
	u	in circus	

Index

A

B

C

Index